Ourselves
and other Animals

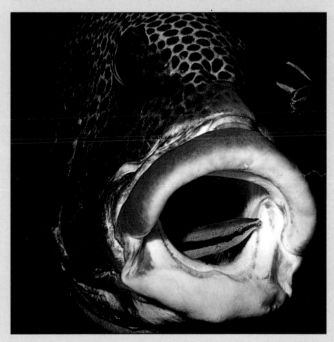

Ourselves and other Animals

From the TV series
with Gerald and Lee Durrell

Peter Evans

INTRODUCTION BY

GERALD DURRELL

0747

PANTHEON BOOKS
NEW YORK

Text © Harcourt Films Ltd,
Primedia Productions Ltd and Primetime Television Ltd 1987
Introduction © Gerald Durrell 1987

All rights reserved under International and
Pan-American Copyright Conventions.
Published in the United States by
Pantheon Books, a division of Random
House, Inc, New York, and simultaneously
in Canada by Random House of Canada
Limited Toronto. Originally published in
Great Britain by Century Hutchinson Ltd.,
London, in 1987

Library of Congress Catalog Card Number: 86-43245
Manufactured in Great Britain

First American Edition

10 9 8 7 6 5 4 3 2 1

Half-title page: Oral hygiene. The cleaner wrasse removes parasites from the mouth of the sweetlips.
Title page: The bright blue male damsel fly – not a female in disguise – in the act of mating. How many females has it already rejected because they looked like males?

Contents

Introduction

In the beginning of our dealings with the other species that inhabit the world with us, animals were viewed as either prey or predator (deer and antelope, sabre-toothed tiger and bear), and, because of their importance to our survival, some assumed supernatural significance for our distant ancestors. As what we are pleased to call civilization progressed and certain animals became domesticated, even some of these retained their magical or religious importance, from cats in Egypt to cows in India. During the Middle Ages in Europe our relationships with the other animals went through the Aesop syndrome, in which various creatures were used to preach moral tales and given human speech and attributes – the cunning fox, the wise old owl, the silly goose. So anthropomorphic was our attitude that some creatures were even accused of witchcraft, like the cats and cockerels which were solemnly tried, condemned and burnt at the stake. Attitudes gradually changed, and in Victorian times, the study of various creatures was approached in a more objective manner, though there was still muddled thinking. Some people viewed animals simply as machines, powered and controlled by a bundle of instincts with none of the human thought processes. We were still using ourselves as yardsticks – a wrong approach to take.

It was only in this century that the science of ethology was born, the meticulous study of animal behaviour, which does not judge the actions of animals against our own skills and abilities. Our whole way of thinking about the creatures around us was revolutionized, because we discovered that their lives were just as intricate and their abilities just as extensive as our own. Not only that, but we could see our own behaviour patterns mirrored in many of the things they did. We were beginning to be forced to acknowledge that we were animals, too – sophisticated ones it is true, but animals none the less – and not the god-like beings that some religious teachings had led us to believe.

We have discovered, for example, that bird-song means something infinitely more complex than birds simply being 'happy'. They use their voices to attract mates, sound alarms, maintain territories and even deceive members of their own and other species. We have discovered that birds have dialects, in the same way that a Scotsman does not speak like a Cornishman, nor someone from Maine like a native of Mississippi. I became aware of this some forty years ago on my first collecting trip to South America. In Guyana there is a bird officially called the tyrant flycatcher, but known locally as the 'qu'est-ce qu'il dit'. Now, I have never been able to reconcile myself to 'humanized' descriptions of bird calls. People assure me that that little finch, the yellowhammer, says 'a little bit of bread and no cheeeeze', but I have never met a specimen that said anything remotely like that. However, in the case of the tyrant flycatcher, I really did hear it say 'qu'est-ce qu'il dit' as clearly as any parrot. Imagine my astonishment then when I went thousands of miles south to Argentina to find the same species of bird, which was not called the 'qu'est-ce qu'il dit', but the 'bichofao'. This bird said just that, as clearly as the 'qu'est-ce qu'il dit' had given its call.

Before ethology became respectable, the study of animal behaviour was, curiously enough, almost ignored by biologists and left to the amateur, so the groundwork for this new and enthralling branch of the biological sciences was left to the bird-watcher, the naturalist and the butterfly collector. It was not until comparatively recently that professional biologists began to regard the amateurs' work as significant, in that they finally accepted the possibility that animals could possess complex sensory, communication and social systems. Although the phrase, commonly used for hundreds of years, 'he went off like a dog with its tail between its legs' was an excellent ethological description of a domestic canine's submissive behaviour, it was a long time before the observation was interpreted as such in studies of grey wolves or African hunting dogs. Then it was found that minute movements of the tail and even the ears were used in a sort of semaphore language.

With the growth of ethology as a science, we have been flooded with a wealth of amazing and wonderful discoveries. We have found that many creatures use technologies that our species has only just invented, such as air-conditioning in termiteries, radar in bats and heatless luminescence in fireflies, and that they can do a great many things that we cannot, like the insects which see ultraviolet light and the dog, whose nose is so sensitive to smells that sniffing round the neighbourhood is as informative as reading the daily newspaper.

Lee and I believe that ethology is one of the most important of the biological sciences, since it teaches us to look more closely at the lives of the other animals around us and to examine more objectively our own behavioural patterns. If we had our way, ethology would form a major portion of any school curriculum.

We hope that this book and the television series on which it is based will give the reader an inkling of the plethora of extraordinary facts that we are now amassing about the behaviour of other animals. Peter Evans has done a splendid job in showing how wide-ranging and fascinating the studies have become. We have discovered that animals do indeed have language, and although it may not resemble human speech in all aspects, it can be a sophisticated means of communication nevertheless, ranging from the language of tail and ears in canids and many other mammals to the scent trails laid down by caterpillars, from the electrical discharges of fish to the duetting of the gibbons.

We have been privileged to listen to animal choruses in various parts of the world. In Madagascar we have been in forests reverberating with the thrilling ululations of the indri, that marvellous great black and white lemur, with prominent golden eyes, penetrating as an accusing judge, and with an agility rarely displayed by any member of the legal profession. Once, a troop of them, sitting in the trees above us, decided to give us the benefit of their beautiful and soulful song. The result was deafening and we felt that if one touched a tree, it would be vibrating like a telegraph pole, but with a message much more interesting. In Panama we have sat enthralled while great roaring waves of sound swept over us, produced by black howler monkeys, proclaiming to each other and for all the world to hear that these were their territories. In our little house in Provence, our ears are battered each summer by the cicadas, the buzzsaws of the olive groves, making the landscape tremble with their mating songs. In the cloud forests of Costa Rica, where each tree wears a coat of moss thicker than a pile carpet, we heard an infinite variety of tinkles, pops, croaks and zithers as the frog and toad populations signalled for partners among the drifting clouds. Snorkelling off Mauritius, the Great Barrier Reef or the San Blas Islands of the Caribbean, we had only to dip our heads beneath the clear warm water and a host of whistles, grunts, purrs and rustles told us that thousands of fish were talking about mates, homes and food.

As well as unravelling the complexities of animal communication, we have discovered a great many other unexpected things about the way animals behave. We have found that many species use tools, for example. Chimpanzees use branches as clubs and grass stalks as 'fishing rods' to extract termites from their nests, vultures use stones to break open the thick-shelled eggs of the ostrich, a finch in the Galapagos uses a thorn to extract beetle larvae from holes in bark, a species of wasp uses a piece of wood to hammer down the earth that covers its nest and eggs, and an ant uses its larvae as sewing machines, holding a grub so it may spin silk to and fro to bind leaves together.

One of the most extraordinary examples of tool-using that I have ever seen concerned a baby orang-utan we had called Oscar. In his cage there was a window with a wooden sill which protruded some two inches from the wall. Leading up to this was an iron ladder with a top rung ending some three inches beneath the overlap of the window sill. Oscar was quite determined to dismantle the window sill, so he would climb up, stand on it, put his fingers under the overlap and tug and tug, but to no avail, since his own weight on the sill defeated his efforts. Nevertheless, he persisted in his proposed demolition work for many weeks, undeterred by lack of success. At that time, we had decided to purchase some large and handsome stainless-steel food dishes for the apes. The first day they were fed in these dishes, I went to watch their reactions. Oscar did something quite astonishing. The plate was no sooner put in his cage than he emptied all the food out of it, carried it across and slid it between the top rung of the ladder and the overlap of the window sill. With a quick downward jerk the whole sill was ripped from its place and Oscar had met with success at last. It was amazing that he had immediately recognized the dish as the tool that had been missing in his efforts to uproot the window sill.

The study of how animals communicate has taught us a lot about ourselves, for we use, in addition to our speech, means of communication also used by other animals. Watch two Italians or two Greeks conversing and you will see body language at its most complex, flamboyant and amusing. But even the less exuberant nationalities such as the English have a body language which one can learn to read. For example, in our series we show a film of how Kim Philby, the spy, gives himself away by minute movements of his face and body when under interrogation. This, of course, was discovered by an expert long after he had defected.

The proper study of mankind is man, so the saying goes. It is certainly fascinating to study your fellow humans if there is no more interesting creature around, and it sometimes saves you from deadly boredom in certain circumstances. I remember once it was politic for me to go to a cocktail party, a thing I abhor. With bad grace I attended. Determined that I would stay the minimum length of time, I got myself a drink and retreated to a corner to play my cocktail party game, which consists of comparing the behaviour of the guests to other animal species. As I was engrossed in this, a very pretty woman with lovely green eyes approached me.

'Hullo,' she said. 'Can I ask you something?'

'By all means,' I said, feeling that the evening might not be a total disaster if I could get into conversation with this delectable lady.

'I've been watching you since you arrived,' she said, 'and you've been scrutinizing everyone as if you were a detective or something. Why?'

I snatched a couple of drinks from a passing waiter and handed her one.

'It's like this,' I confided. 'I hate cocktail parties, particularly dreary and boring ones like this. So if I am forced to come to them, I play my cocktail party game to prevent myself from dying of ennui.'

'What's your cocktail party game?' she asked, looking slightly taken aback.

'Comparing human behaviour to the behaviour of other animals and spotting the similarities. Look over there, for example, the way that man in the yellow tie keeps puffing himself up and stepping between his wife and any man who comes up to them, and clenching his hands. A display of male dominance, similar to ones you can see among most primates. See that chap over there who keeps feeding *hors d'oeuvres* to that girl? Well, some male penguins – who have the good sense not to go to cocktail parties – nevertheless give little tokens of esteem to the lady of their choice, only in the penguins' case the gifts are pebbles and not sausages on sticks.'

'Fascinating,' said the lady, her eyes twinkling with amusement. 'Tell me more.' So for the next ten minutes I regaled her with my observations.

'It's the only thing to do at a cocktail party to remain sane,' I said at last. 'Look, this is without doubt the dullest gathering of its sort I have ever been to. Why don't we cut and run and I'll give you dinner somewhere nice?'

'I'd love to,' she said wistfully, 'but I don't think I can.'

'Oh, come on,' I said impatiently. 'Leave all these bores to this dreadful party and come with me.'

'No, really, I don't think I can,' she said.

'Why not?' I demanded.

'Well, I *am* the hostess, you see,' she explained.

It was obvious I had not been watching her body language nearly closely enough, and the next morning it cost me a fortune in flowers (at least pebbles for penguins are free!) to try to eradicate my *faux pas*.

Gerald Durrell

Jersey, Channel Islands
October 1986

Chapter One

Links in
a Universal
Chain

1 April 2087. It is a momentous day, perhaps even, as the media are suggesting, the most important in the history of the Earth. It is the day that the International Space Agency's first fully operational space colony – ISACOL One – receives official recognition as an independent body. After today's ceremony, ISACOL One becomes to all intents and purposes a little self-governing planet in its own right. Getting to this point has been a long haul. After decades of space engineering and communications technology research, followed by yet more decades of intensively mining the moons of Mars, Phobos and Deimos for the metals and other raw materials required to construct this vast orbiting home for 20,000 people, working plans had to be finalized. How to organize the living and working quarters; how to administer the shops, hospitals, computer networks and the million and one other necessary services; how to feed the hungry, growing population of space pioneers that will eventually fill the great wheeling space vehicle to capacity. Now, however, all that is over and ISACOL One proudly orbits Saturn, operationally autonomous, self-sufficient in food produced from its extensive farms and biological protein fermenters. As the commission from Earth arrives to grant the new colony independent planetary status, the air is abuzz with self-congratulations.

But suddenly one of the incoming delegation – not a dignitary but a biologist here to meet members of the ISACOL Academy of Sciences – begins to feel uneasy. As the party strolls along the automated polymer walkways and marvels at the solar conversion power stations, she realizes, with a prickling at the back of the neck, that something is missing, something without which it is impossible to imagine any community being able to flourish. What ISACOL One lacks, apart from the micro-organisms working away in the food fermenters or those that infect patients in the infirmaries is . . . animals. A horrible mistake has been made.

ISACOL One is, of course, an imaginary space colony. But the loss to humanity of being without animals would be very real. We share our planet with animals in so many ways. Like them we form a link, for example, in a complex food chain with organism feeding on organism feeding on organism in an ecologically-balanced fashion. Take away animals and the loss to the ecosystem would be incalculable. From a purely human standpoint, it is not simply that we would have to forgo the arguable pleasure of eating animal protein. A world devoid of charbroiled steaks, hamburgers and fish fingers would be tolerable: some would say desirable. Nor would the loss be only one of companionship and comfort derived from keeping pets, although this would indeed be regrettable. The real deprivation goes deeper than that.

Pictures from a family album

'What a piece of work is Man!' wrote Shakespeare, 'How noble in reason!' Warming to this theme of self-adulation, he goes on: 'The beauty of the world! The paragon of animals!' Even in this fine piece of human-centred, opinionated rhetoric there is, nevertheless, a reminder that we *are* animals. Some of the other sentiments might be disputed, but of this there can be no doubt. We are animals in a world of other animals: members of a huge extended family. Lacking either them or ourselves, our world would be incomplete.

This book, as its title suggests, attempts to set us in our family context. More specifically, it is about a particularly fascinating form of behaviour that links us inextricably to our animal relatives: communication. It is, then, a book about how animals communicate with each other, and we with them; and in what ways our uses of communication are similar. Why, though, should this subject matter to us? After all, do we not already have enough problems trying to make contact with one another, let alone worrying about the signals that pass between species which appear to have little in common with us anyway? So what makes animal communication so relevant to us?

There are three reasons which we might encapsulate in three words: context, utility and insight. Let us look at them briefly in that order.

Tongues, tennis courts and our animal context

The study of animal behaviour constantly reveals similarities between species; and in those similarities we might perceive patterns. Take, for example, the observation made by Dr Julia Chase, a biologist at Barnard College in New York, one day at the zoo. She happened to be watching gorillas walking, carefully balanced, along a fence and noticed that these animals almost invariably had their tongues lolling out. It reminded her of the time she worked in nursery schools where young children, when balancing on a play-frame, would likewise stick out their tongue. Being an inquisitive scientist, Julia Chase asked the obvious question: why? As she did so, it occurred to her that sportsmen and women, too, use their tongues in this way. When John McEnroe stretches up to serve, the tongue that has lashed many an umpire silently flicks out as an accompaniment to the shot.

Armed with these thoughts, she took herself off to local pool halls and watched players at the table. Whenever they settled down to a shot, out would come the tongue as if to say 'This is tricky'. She then decided to study other groups of people concentrating on their endeavours, including browsers in pornographic magazine shops. Again, tongues were much in evidence. Once she noticed an old lady crossing the road in front of her car when the light changed to 'Don't walk'. The pedestrian turned to her and out came the tongue, indicating this time, it seemed, something different: not 'I'm concentrating', but 'Please do not interfere, I'm doing something important.'

Thus from the notion that sticking out the tongue means simply that the individual is concentrating, Dr Chase moved on to a related idea: that the tongue is a non-verbal signal to others, indicating 'Keep off. This is no time for social interaction.' Another group of researchers devised an ingenious experiment to test this idea in a controlled way. They gave a group of students in a classroom an exam paper, telling them to complete every page. The

Non-verbal communication. Tongue out, John McEnroe prepares to serve.

Varieties of nuisance. The lapwing (*above*), starling (*right*) and black-headed gull (*below*) may all be controlled by 'bio-acoustic' scaring methods that exploit directly the alarm language of each species.

students found, however, that page three was missing, so they had to consult their professor. At this point the teacher either had his tongue protruding or not. This had an immediate effect on their readiness to approach him and on the time spent with him. Thus, says Julia Chase, the protruding tongue is a mild signal sent out, unconsciously, to others by all age groups, and very quickly drawing a response when detected. From a chance observation of a gorilla, therefore, she and other researchers have been able to identify another item in the catalogue of complex non-verbal messages exchanged between humans. We have, in this instance, been able to learn a little more about ourselves by starting with another species.

The redundant scarecrow

Learning about how animals communicate can be useful even to the point of saving human lives. On 13 November 1980, a four-engined Nimrod aircraft, taking off in virtual darkness from RAF Kinloss, struck a flock of black-headed gulls. It crashed, killing two crew members and costing the RAF an estimated £20 million in damaged equipment. One month later, black-headed gulls were again struck by an aircraft in flight, this time a Boeing 737 with 120 passengers on board. Luckily, no one was hurt, but the two engines had to be changed, so damaged were they by this perilous impact.

Bird strikes are just one of the ways in which birds represent a nuisance, and gulls are but one of the offending species; lapwings and starlings, too, feed or rest near airfields and are a potential aircraft hazard. Farmers, of course, have known for many centuries that a whole host of bird species find their crops a source of nourishment, despite the presence of a stick-and-cloth human effigy in the form of a scarecrow.

Both kinds of nuisance are being countered thanks to a growing knowledge of bird-to-bird communication. When a bird sees a prey or some other hazard, it emits a distinctive alarm call. These distress calls are very specific in character and, like a human scream, leave the hearer in no doubt whatsoever that something is very much amiss and that this is a place to avoid. Researchers have therefore resorted to 'bio-acoustic' methods to minimize the risk to aircraft. By recording these scare calls and playing them at chosen times around airfields, they have been able to reduce the numbers of bird strikes appreciably. Similarly, experiments are now being carried out to control crop pests with species-specific alarm calls played from loudspeakers around cornfields and orchards. These techniques are much more powerful than, say, a generalized siren-like warning or the old-fashioned scarecrow because the sounds broadcast across field or airport speak directly to the target birds. It is their own distress call. We are talking to them in their own language for our own utilitarian ends.

On the scent of new therapies

We share with animals a number of ways of communicating. We, like them, can vocalize or impart non-verbal messages. We can send signals by light and telegraph as can some animal species; and so on. There is, however, one form of communication widely used by other creatures that only very recently we have come to appreciate may also be shared by humans in quite powerful yet subtle ways. It is based on smell. Animals as diverse as house-mice, sheep, ants and salmon secrete odiferous substances called pheromones that have a strong influence upon the behaviour of other individuals of the same kind.

Indeed, there are whole 'languages' based on these meaningful social odours. They can contain shades of meaning that might seem to us, with our greatly diminished sense of smell (what the blind Helen Keller called the 'fallen angel of the senses'), totally beyond our experience. However, behavioural scientists such as Dr Gary Schwartz of Yale University believe that the sense of smell may be more important to us than we tend to think. It is not just the sensory channel that allows us the pleasure of savouring fresh-brewed coffee or exquisite perfumes. It may also be a route to physical and emotional health. Dr Schwartz finds that pleasant familiar odours such as that of spiced apples seem to induce a relaxation response in stressed individuals akin to that produced by say, transcendental meditation. Blood pressure can be brought down by such smells, he contends, while others believe that allergies and headaches, too, can be alleviated by 'aromatherapy'.

At the Duke University Medical Center, Dr Susan Schiffman has developed taste sprays to reduce food cravings in obese people. Because taste is primarily dictated by smell (which is why a blocked nose during a cold will take away all taste of food) Dr Schiffman finds she can satisfy craving by odour alone. One company, Environmental Fragrance Technologies, markets aroma discs together with a special player to waft a variety of odours, from 'Victorian Garden' to 'After Dinner-Mints', into the home at the touch of a button. Meanwhile, neuro-scientists, studying the mechanisms by which brain cells receive and react to olfactory stimuli, are, together with psychologists, learning more about the nature of behaviour-shaping chemicals. These, among humans as in animals, may be involved in all sorts of important interactions, both positive and negative. Chemical or odour cues may partly provide the explanation for the bonding of two lovers or for the discord of baby battering.

Salmonspeak. Leaping salmon in a mountain stream, Wales. These fish secrete chemicals for communication purposes.

Similar but not the same

There are thousands of ways in which the study of animal communication may have something novel, important or fascinating to say to us about our own behaviour. In fact, this book constantly points to parallels, comparisons and analogies between human and non-human communication techniques and strategies. It should be remembered, nevertheless, that these are only comparisons. They are not necessarily an attempt to explain all our human conduct by reference to that of other species. Indeed, it would be not merely unscientific but downright foolhardy to do so.

One of the fiercest debates in the whole field of science at present is about this very question of the extent to which we can explain human behaviour by reference to biological mechanisms seen operating elsewhere in the animal kingdom. The extreme 'socio-biological' lobby suggests that this may be the case, though certainly not to the extent that is often popularly inferred. There is no scientific basis for the wrongheaded notion that such undesirable traits as racism and xenophobia, for example, find echoes in other species for good evolutionary reasons. Therefore, we should regard these as wholly 'natural' and, by implication, excusable or less-than-reprehensible when seen at work in the human animal species. This is a gross misrepresentation of the socio-biological viewpoint.

Opponents of socio-biology though claim that it still overstates a case. Although we are, like other species, shaped by millennia of evolution, human beings, they assert, differ from other animals in a number of important ways, having acquired culture, moral and ethical systems, and a number of other social constraints on undesirable behaviour. Evolution, as expressed in our genes, can to a large extent be overridden.

This is, in truth, a simplification of a complex scientific debate but it does draw our attention to one fundamental point: that there are limits to the comparisons one can draw between species. Beware those ethologists who, having observed the courting behaviour of fish or the infant-parent interactions of birds, see biological mechanisms that could be generalized throughout the animal kingdom, including humankind. Dr Richard Dawkins, rejecting this buckshot-style over-generalization, writes: '. . . the thing that interests me most is to apply to humans not the detailed facts of other species' behaviour, nor the observational methods developed for studying other species, but the *principles* that apply to all living things, regardless of the details of a particular application to particular species.'

These are the limits of ethology. We can, if we are lucky, detect in the behaviour of other animals the broad, underlying organizational principles that may govern *our* behaviour. But we should not look elsewhere for insights into human behaviour that can only be explained in the context of human behaviour itself. A number of biologists have tried, for example, to 'explain' the aggressive side of human nature in ethological terms, pointing to the many manifestations of aggressive and cooperative behaviour in animals, and jumping from here to *Homo sapiens* in one imaginative step. The gap is too wide.

According to Professor Patrick Bateson of Cambridge University, ethology does have a big role to play in helping us to solve the problems of humanity. 'The use of simpler animals to solve some complex problems of social behaviour is very much on the cards . . . They focus our minds on particular issues which it's very difficult to have focused if we deal simply with the complexity of human nature.' However, that is a long way, according

Symbolic animals: in India the sacred cow is further dignified by a statue; in the West the bull lends its name to stocks and shares moving up in price.

to Pat Bateson, from being able to 'explain' why we act in precisely the way we do. 'When one's asked,' he says, 'some very specific problems like why should you behave competitively in one set of circumstances and cooperatively in another, the answers that you come up with in the case of one animal are going to be very different from the answers you come up with in the case of another animal.'

A sense of wonder

Perhaps, though, at the end of the day, the best reason for taking an interest in how other animals communicate has nothing to do with any practical advantages, self-analysis or personal insight this might confer. Perhaps it is for the same reason that the mountaineer risks his neck to climb a peak or the lone sailor to circumnavigate the Earth: because it is there. The genuine lover of animal behaviour will understand immediately this drive to explore. The bird-watcher squatting in wellington boots on a damp mud-flat waiting for a sighting; the primatologist carefully recording and replaying the chattering of monkeys in an attempt to find 'speech' patterns; the insect expert fascinated by endless examples of sophisticated social organization in tiny creatures with minute and primitive brains. All these need no justification for their patience and application beyond the joy of observation.

In *The Myth of the Machine* Lewis Mumford muses on the spiritual deprivation humanity might have suffered had it been born in a different, unnatural setting. If mankind had originally inhabited a world as drab as a high-rise housing development, or as lifeless as an automatic factory, it is doubtful, he argues, whether we would have acquired 'sufficiently varied experience to retain images, mould a language, or acquire ideas'. If we have escaped that fate, it is because we inhabit a living world, brought to life by the animals that surround us. Animals mould our thoughts and imaginings in many different and subtle ways. Investors on the stock market have their own little menagerie, describing trading conditions as 'bullish' or 'bearish'; while many religions endow animals – cows, birds, lions – with sacred characteristics.

It was in recognition of our interdependence with animals that, when NASA launched its two Voyager spacecraft, destined ultimately for distant stars and galaxies, affixed to each vehicle was a gold-plated copper disc carrying a recording of the sounds of our planet, including music and languages of many cultures. As well as greetings in 60 human tongues, there is another word of hello on that interstellar journey. It is from one humpback whale to another. If and when some remote extra-terrestrial civilization comes to play the record and consider its contents, perhaps they too will wonder, as we have done, at these ineffably marvellous sounds. They may even envy us for having such expressive relatives.

Chapter Two

Them and Us?

High on a bleak hillside a watchful shepherd lets out a series of three sharp whistles. Downwind, several hundred yards away across the rock and heather, his dog moves rapidly to the left. Then, suddenly, it crouches down, waiting for the next instruction. Meanwhile the large, straggling flock of sheep has lurched round to form a neat, compact group, assembled now in orderly fashion ready to pass through the gate to the next field. All it has taken to organize, indeed manipulate, the movements of the sheep has been a brief signal from man to dog.

To the uninitiated, so much control from so little effort seems almost miraculous; and in a sense it is. For we have just witnessed a remarkable and intricate communications network in action. It is remarkable not merely because communication here is occurring in a variety of channels. After all, in a world of radio and television, satellites and computers, telex machines and telephones, we are familiar with a multiplicity of ways of linking A to B to C. What distinguishes the interplay of shepherd, dog and sheep is that it is taking place between different *species*.

Consider exactly what has happened. From a thought in the farmer's head ('Time to move into the next pasture') is generated a signal to the dog, which naturally has an entirely different kind of mental apparatus. Nevertheless, the signal does realize the man's objective, because he has forsaken his own language temporarily to 'talk' in terms his dog can comprehend. But it goes a stage further. The dog, for its part, has also 'spoken' to the sheep, not by barking, but with the gestural language of body movement. So an idea in the mind of the shepherd has been transferred, to all intents and purposes, into the collective consciousness of his sheep, using a third-party species as interpreter.

Back to the pen: a Welsh sheep-dog at work. From puppies, sheep-dogs will naturally assume the typical herding stance.

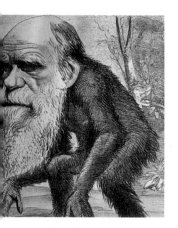

Charles Darwin as caricatured in *The Hornet* in 1871. The idea of humans having a primate ancestry created uproar from the cartoonist to the clergy.

It could, of course, be argued that the control exercised by the shepherd over dog and flock is nothing more than the product of clever training. The dog does not, in any human sense of the word, understand its master's objectives. It cares not one jot about the need to round up sheep for economic grazing purposes. It is simply responding to predetermined signals which it has been taught to recognize and act upon after many repeated hours of practice. The sheep are even less aware of what is happening. They merely see the dog as a threat, so they do the wise thing and move along.

In other words, to use the phrase 'communication between species' in this context seems somewhat exaggerated. Communication, for us, implies exchanging underlying thoughts, expressing feelings, intentions and ambitions, not just words or symbols. There has to be content and meaning as well as form. Most people think that no such interchange takes place between ourselves and animals, or between individual animals.

Yet this notion, which has been held for centuries and is still widely accepted, is seriously open to question. The more we examine it, the less convincing it seems. Animals display an astounding variety of subtle expressions and strategies for making contact with one another as well as with us. As communicators, animals are proving to be far cleverer than we have ever admitted. As we shall see later, from the simplest organisms right up to our closest relatives, the great apes, communication plays just as important a part in the life of animals as it does in ours. Indeed, without the capacity for exchanging information at a variety of levels, most species would simply die out. Nature has little, if any, room for isolationism.

Unkind humankind

It is only quite recently, at least in *our* culture, that humans have even begun to recognize, let alone respect, these abilities among the vast array of animals on this planet. Traditionally, perhaps before Charles Darwin's ideas on the evolution of all species began to take root, we tended to regard ourselves as inherently superior to the beasts of the field, to consider humankind as the highpoint of creation, looking down on the grovelling, mindless mass of animals as base incompetents.

True, we have at times allowed them the somewhat doubtful pleasure of human company by making pets of them. Yet the man-animal relationship has, for the most part, been akin to that of noble lord and feudal serf. We have a long history of treating animals as disposable chattels. The 18th-century poet William Somerville, an enthusiastic huntsman, echoed centuries of opinion when he wrote:

> 'The brute creation are his property,
> Subservient to his will, and for him made.
> As hurtful these he kills, as useful those
> Preserves: the sole and arbitrary king.'

This kind of superiority complex seems to go back a very long way. It also has a strong religious flavouring. Remember, for example, the biblical Book of Genesis. In the Garden of Eden, Adam, though living peacefully together with all living things, still enjoyed God-given dominion over them. Come the Fall and the relationship changed. Insects and other pests appeared. Creatures became fierce and aggressive towards their former master. The loss of the earthly Paradise was typified by the sheer fact that animals were behaving . . . like animals! Luckily, after the Flood, God restored to humanity some of its lost authority by once more giving us complete sway over all that moved on the earth, flew in the sky or swam in the sea. Even so, the original calm relationship in the Garden of Eden was never recaptured. From then on, and in an unbroken tradition right up to our own time, it would seem we have endeavoured to assert our authority, perhaps subconsciously to overcome our fear of animals, by doing our utmost to tame or hunt them into submission.

There can be no more graphic illustration of this than the sight of the tightly suited Victorian aristocrat, one carefully polished boot (fashioned, naturally, from the hide of some animal) poised on the carcass of a large mammal, such as an elephant or leopard, killed in the course of a hunting party in India or Africa. There is much symbolism in that self-satisfied snapshot of the imperial past which goes beyond the scene it depicts. It is almost as if the marksman were regarding the hunt as a microcosm of the social structure of the Empire. He is the dominating leader, asserting his rights over an inferior opponent. The prey has come to stand for a whole continent and its human population.

Animal and people have here become indistinguishable, as indeed in the days of American slavery, when a healthy male would be sold as a 'strong, young buck negro', there being in the minds of the white trader no distinction between inferior human and animal. Such has been the confusion in the minds of our predecessors that history records some ludicrously inappropriate behaviour: animals, including caterpillars, have been tried and sentenced in human courts; eels were once excommunicated; and less than eighty years

King George V, on a visit to Nepal in 1912, personally killed three tigers and three rhinoceroses on the first day's shooting. Colossal bags of this kind have decimated animal populations: only 45 rhinos are now left in the wild in Nepal.

ago dogs were being condemned to death in European courtrooms –
instances where the celebrated blindness of Justice was accompanied by total
stupidity masquerading under a guise of rectitude!

Asserting superiority

There are striking similarities between our punitive treatment of animals
and those individuals we have deemed to be 'second class citizens'. The
wholesale slaughter of wild animals, hunted to the point of extinction,
finds an echo, for example, in the savage extermination of the indigenous
population of North America by the invading Europeans. Just as the carefully
poised ecosystem of jungle or forest was to be shattered by the great white
hunter with his relentless use of firearms, so too the deeply held religious
and cultural values of the North American Indians, with their wealth of
languages and reverence for sacred landmarks and animal spirits, were
wiped away in a virtual holocaust.

In both cases – the hunting of animals and genocide – the underlying
assumption is that, in the spectrum of Creation, there is a natural hierarchy,
with an élite at the top and the rest forming a vast 'proletariat'. Like the pigs
in George Orwell's *Animal Farm*, we appear to subscribe to the motto that
'some are more equal than others'. Just as astronomers used to believe, on
the evidence of their eyes prior to the invention of telescopes, that the Earth
was the very centre of the Universe, so too was it commonly believed that
what was not human was unworthy, peripheral, even irrelevant to the central
drama of life.

Such arrogance was carried to the extremes of absurdity by certain
enlightened souls who contended that animals had been carefully designed
by the hand of a discriminating God exclusively concerned with human
needs and wishes. Some even argued that the Creator had sensibly stocked
our planet with fewer ferocious animals than docile species, and organized
matters so that the wilder animals only came out at night when mankind was
safely tucked up in bed. One doctor in the early 18th century seriously came
up with the ingenious notion that the good Lord made the excrement of
horses smell pleasant because He knew that humans would often be in
contact with it! Once you start thinking along these lines there is no end to
the sorts of human-centred explanations you can come up with: that horse
flies have been made irritating in order to test the wits of humans; that apes
and parrots exist solely to entertain us; even that cattle and sheep were given
life in order to keep their meat fresh until we were ready to partake of it.
God thus uses the animal kingdom to become, in turn, and for our sole
benefit, schoolmaster, showman and restaurateur.

Killing fields

Against this kind of background it is easy to see why in the past we have had
so little compunction about blithely eliminating animals of all shapes, sizes
and habitats. It simply did not matter. So when the great Elizabethan sailors
such as Hawkins encountered huge flocks of penguins, a bird they had never
seen before, and one equally unaccustomed to the presence of humans, their
first reactions, apparently, were to slaughter them in their hundreds. Strolling
through some remote jungle, the explorer of the past had just enough time
to marvel at the brilliant plumage of a novel exotic bird, or the movements
of an unusual small mammal before lifting his shotgun and consigning them
to oblivion. It was a matter of honour for Lord Spencer, an English aristocrat,

A bird that has flown for good. The great auk became extinct as early as 1844, victim of the mindless hunter.

to offer his royal guest Charles I a banquet in 1634 which featured literally dozens of wild birds on the menu including ruffs, reeves, redshanks, herons, storks, godwits, dotterels and a number of other species nowadays extinct in Britain. No wonder, with appetites of that kind!

Evidently, the bigger the game, the greater the relish for the hunter. But the thrill has been costly for the animals on the receiving end. The great elk of Ireland, the cave bear and the great bustard have now gone for good, extinct in the name of sport. Not that recreation is invariably the sole intention. Fox-hunters would argue that they are exterminating an undeniable farm pest, as well as reducing the risk of rabies, a killer disease carried by foxes throughout Europe. Superficially it seems a reasonable plea until you think of the tiny impact on the fox population produced by an afternoon's hunt. Considering that the only kill is an exhausted, terrified animal, one cannot help but agree with Oscar Wilde that fox-hunting is the 'unspeakable in pursuit of the uneatable', or perhaps more to the point so far as the anti-pest lobby is concerned, 'the ineffectual in pursuit of the innumerable'.

Animals as entertainment

Much as we have delighted in killing animals, there have always been some people who have paused just long enough to assert their superiority in another way; by capturing their prey. Zoos, menageries and travelling animal shows became particularly popular in the 19th century; but they were not, as now, designed primarily to give the public an opportunity to wonder at the scale and diversity of nature. Judging by the sizes of the animal cages then in use, the real object was to give the visitor that vicarious thrill engendered by being close to, but not threatened by, a dangerous or bizarre animal. Nowadays we have become so familiar with, say, the lion or the vulture through television and films that it is hard to imagine the feelings of our predecessors as they peered into the zoo cage, sampling the unfamiliar smell, perhaps thrilling at the sense of thwarted power as the exhibit paced up and down or fluttered sporadically in its cramped, circumscribed space. One might make another comparison with those Sunday afternoon strollers who, only a century or so ago, would spend a couple of hilarious hours at London's famous Bethlem Hospital – a 'lunatic asylum' – watching the grimaces and gestures of the mentally-sick inmates. The pleasure derived from gaping at people locked in the confines of a troubled mind was on a par with the entertaining sight of tightly caged jungle animals. In either case the motive perhaps was not so much cruelty as fear, the feeling – and it is with us still – that 'there but for the grace of God go I'; fear, too, that unless the unfamiliar, foreign and remote are kept at arm's length, we may all be contaminated by them.

Yet, for all its mindlessness, the undesirable treatment of zoo animals is perhaps preferable to our exploitation of other species as entertainment acts. Though caged, a zoo animal is at least left alone to salvage from the environment what remains of its own identity. In circuses and vaudeville, with their frightful animal acts, the whole object of the exercise seems to be to persuade other species to behave in a crude approximation of ourselves. Dogs wearing an Egyptian fez and riding a bicycle; elephants dressed in ballerinas' tutus, perched on tiny pedestals; conjuring seals; calculating pigeons; horses dancing a travesty of the foxtrot or quickstep. When the thunderous applause dies away, one is left wondering just what it is we are really appreciating. Surely it is not the cleverness of the animal. No canine cyclist will win the Tour de France, no ballet-dancing elephant will appear at Covent Garden, and no mathematical pigeon will ever claim a Nobel Prize. As surrogate humans, circus animals make a pretty poor show.

What we are really enjoying, perhaps, is the skill of the animals' trainers in diverting the innate capabilities of their charges to human ends. But allied to that is our wish for the performing animal to look gauche, silly or even grotesque, underlining how far beneath us it really is in the order of things. It simply would not do for any animal to upstage a human. So in the guise of entertainment we are once more trying to maintain what we imagine to be our rightful species-supremacy. The only purpose in this form of communication with animals is to humiliate or exploit them.

A prolific resource

On the other hand, we have long realized, with characteristically human foresight, that animals are an important economic resource. Without them, life for us would be a good deal harder. It is difficult, in fact, to picture a world where animals did not figure prominently in providing us with food, shelter, labour and other services, including companionship. At its best, the man-animal relationship can work extremely well, to the benefit of both parties. At worst, it is an opportunity for exercising some of our deeply rooted anti-animal feelings.

For a positive example we need look no further than the shepherd with his dog and his flock. The sheep is a prolific source of meat and clothing, but it needs to be encouraged, by thoughtful husbandry, to provide maximum yield. So the farmer, be he a smallholder in the Scottish highlands or an

Australian rancher with thousands of acres at his disposal, must be in tune with the natural needs of his animals. He has to allow his sheep enough time and freedom to reproduce, rest and graze. He must key his demands for meat or wool into the cycles of nature. It simply will not work if he goes too far in forcing rhythms evolved over millions of years into the artificial tempos of man-made society.

Nevertheless, the attempt has been made to do just that, to straitjacket the animal kingdom into an existence that is exclusively designed for 'productivity', 'yield' and all the other features so dear to the hearts of accountants. It is called, appropriately, battery farming; and it bears as much resemblance to the caring kind of man-animal relationship established by the shepherd as the vast, impersonal shopping mall or hypermarket does to the village grocery shop. The logical extension of the battery system, row upon cramped row of egg-laying creatures with no experience or notion of pecking freely around in the farmyard, is the kind of biological nightmare threatened by geneticists.

Obviously, to be fully efficient economically, the battery chicken needs redesigning. It hardly requires legs, wings or beaks, or any other feature redundant to the producer's purposes. It simply has to be a body for ingesting nutrients and converting these into eggs or flesh. So why not, with the aid of sophisticated (and as yet, thankfully, undiscovered) genetic methods, breed chickens to be just that? An artist's impression of such a living machine would be enough to turn the stomach of any omelette lover or fried-chicken eater. But were such an automaton ever to see the artificial light, it would, of course, remain hidden for tasteful cosmetic reasons.

Fortunately, we are far removed from this extreme. Although agricultural practices have been mechanized to the point that farming is now a genuine industry, it still makes sense for the farmer to treat his animals with the respect and sensitivity we associate with the bygone days of small mixed herds, hand-milking and ample time to lean on the stile and exchange tales of rustic folklore. Nor is there any reason why the man-animal relationship should not be enhanced, rather than diminished, by increased technological innovation.

Conveyor-belt production of eggs from battery chickens. The 'need' for high productivity in the farming industry is pursued regardless of the stress and discomfort of the 'labour force'.

Friendly robots

Take, for example, the dairy cow. As a rule, the cow to be milked is herded into the milking parlour twice a day, its udders heavy with up to 25 pounds (11.3 kg) of fluid from which it is aching to be relieved. Now this is unsatisfactory. Experiments have shown that, given the choice, the cow would prefer to be milked more than twice a day, i.e. 'on demand'. But herding cows takes time and expensive labour. For this reason, at laboratories such as the British National Institute of Agricultural Engineering, research is currently under way to devise a genuine robot milker. The idea is for the cow to make its way whenever it wishes into the milking parlour. There it begins to eat, while a sensitive transponder identifies it by means of a special code through a computer. Having identified the individual cow, the computer tells the milking machine precisely which configuration of clusters to attach to the four teats. It is of crucial importance that the cluster 'fingerprint' in the computer matches that of the particular cow, otherwise the animal will resent the robot's attempts to extract milk from her.

Many attempts, too, are being made to ensure that animals remain healthy by the application of a whole range of preventive medical techniques, such as vaccination, regular checkups, and antenatal monitoring. Perhaps one day we shall see as wide a range of health-care services for animals as we ourselves enjoy; and perhaps it will include not only physical but also psychiatric care. For if the tag 'Mens sana in corpore sano' ('A healthy mind in a healthy body') holds true for us, why not for animals as well? It may be that behavioural scientists of the future will find it profitable to turn their attentions to animal psychology, to explore the limits of horse sense, the sentiment behind a bovine stare or the social needs of flocks of sheep – all with a view to maintaining the psychological health of valuable farm stock. Could there already be, somewhere, a new Sigmund Freud, determined to investigate in depth the psyches of geese, chickens and lambs in the interests of good farming practice? It may seem a fanciful and even ludicrous idea, until you appreciate how far researchers have gone in revealing the extent of animal thought and animal consciousness. It is a topic we shall be returning to in some detail in Chapter Twelve.

Power to our elbows

For almost as long as men have been rearing animals for food and clothing, they have also been using them as workmates: horses and oxen to pull ploughs and shift loads; camels, yaks and elephants to transport people or goods across rugged and hostile terrains; dogs tugging carts and sledges; mules laden with huge bales of hay. Even Santa Claus, that indefatigable purveyor of toys to the children of the world, would be grounded without the haulage service provided by his aerobatic reindeer.

In this area, too, the relationship has not always been marked by understanding and consideration. With the rapidly accelerating growth of factories during the Industrial Revolution, accompanied by the insatiable need for fuel to keep the furnaces and chimneys active, coal assumed supreme economic importance. So too did the wretched pit pony, small enough to negotiate the low overhangs of subterranean tunnels, and strong

The shark is an animal that incites fear and apprehension, even though, statistically speaking, humans have little cause to worry about sharks swimming nearby. Here the grey shark hunts in the Red Sea off the Sudan.

enough to drag great quantities of gritty, choking coal back to the shaft. The alienation and stress these creatures endured boggles the mind. Not that things were any better for their human companions. In the days before mechanization, man and animal were equally disadvantaged in their troglo-dytic environment. Both were practically depersonalized, mere automata, working, eating, resting, working in a relentless cycle throughout the whole of a comparatively short life.

By and large, however, we have come to realize, like the farmer with his livestock, that a working animal becomes a far more valuable resource if it is treated humanely and with due regard to its particular needs. Again George Orwell in *Animal Farm* captures the point with his portrayal of the indomitable Boxer, the massive farm horse who symbolizes the working class in the revolutionary overthrow of a tyrannical regime. It is Boxer who pushes himself willingly to prodigious lengths in his daily toil, motivated by a belief in what he is doing. Although Orwell intends us to think of Boxer as an allegorical representation of the decent working man and woman, he is also telling us a lot about successful working relationships between man and animal. Briefly, his lesson is that the carrot is better than the stick. Give an animal (or a person) encouragement by way of reward and its work rate can be stupendous. Positive reinforcement, to use the psychologists' jargon, works far better than a negative or aversive stimulus.

Bulk transport, Moroccan-style. The donkey's capacity for bearing heavy loads has been recognized and exploited for thousands of years.

The same is true of all working animals, be they humble carthorses or multi-million-dollar thoroughbred stallions; farm dogs or Greyhound Derby hopefuls. Performance or productivity are almost invariably a direct measure of the owner's or trainer's sensitivity to an animal's needs.

It is difficult to estimate the contribution that the animal kingdom makes to our lives. Apart from the obvious benefits of livestock reared for food and clothing, there are less hard-nosed but equally valuable reasons why we should be grateful for the existence of other species on this planet.

Man, myth and monster

Without animals our planet would be strangely lacking in all kinds of symbolic and mythological colour. Through animals we have come to understand more about some of the more shadowy recesses of our psychological selves. We transmute our deep-seated aversion to all that is 'wild' and 'untamed', for example, into fictional forms, and serve it up in stories such as Tarzan. The spectacle of our muscular hero wrestling with a lion or some other predatory beast is a modern version of a medieval stage allegory in which Good is pitted against Evil.

Similarly, an animal-centred drama can re-create that vague sense of unease we all experience at the ill-defined, yet powerful images and feelings stirred up in a bad dream. Think of the giant shark in *Jaws*; the monstrous squid attacking the Nautilus in Jules Verne's *20,000 Leagues Under The Sea*; the baying of the hound of the Baskervilles, and so on. We use animals, rightly or wrongly, to give form to feelings of indefinable disquiet that go even deeper than this. Many of us will have watched with growing apprehension the ominous flocks in Alfred Hitchcock's movie *The Birds* or shared Winston Smith's revulsion to rats in George Orwell's *1984*, but not really understanding how and why these animalistic suggestions were creating such a powerful impact.

We have a very long history of using animals as a mirror of our intimate psyches. Animal spirit worship is commonplace in all tribal cultures while, in Greek mythology, the two-headed dog Cerberus, the writhing snakes in the head of Medusa and the great Kraken guarding the undersea domain, are all attempts to give physical form to what are essentially non-physical phenomena, namely the thoughts and feelings that populate the spectacular scenarios of the unconscious.

Not that all our symbolic representations of animals are necessarily murky or negative. Animals, for instance, figure prominently in heraldry as the embodiment of all the virtues theoretically associated with great aristocratic families. The lion in particular, synonymous with strength, courage and nobility, appears frequently on crests and shields. Even the dragon, a beast with a very bad public relations image by reason of its appetite for humans, is deemed worthy of portrayal on a heraldic shield, presumably for its vigour and ferocity: a clear case of accentuating the positive temporarily at the expense of the negative.

Our treatment of animals, in fiction and myth as in real life, is continuously ambivalent. We love them and hate them, admire and fear, glorify and suppress. At the bullfight, one half of the spectator thrills to the sight of a massive, proud animal directing its superhuman strength at a frail matador. The other delights in the supremacy of mind over matter, in the spectacle of a balletic performer calmly delivering the *coup de grâce* to an exhausted, crazed, beaten opponent in an unequal struggle. The very animals that are cuddly, charming, amusing, heroic in children's stories are the source of powerful adult fears and phobias. Psychiatric textbooks are full of them: cynophobia (dogs), alektorophobia (chickens), hippophobia (horses), and many more. Strange to think that for some people Lassie, Chicken Licken and Black Beauty are as terrifying as any unearthly beast dreamed up by ancient mythologists.

Certain animals are hardly recognizable as the same species when viewed from the different perspectives of fiction or fable. The humble and serene goat, source of protein, milk and cheese, has his horns transplanted on to the head of the Devil; and the bat becomes the alternative physical form of the blood-thirsty Count Dracula.

In such contexts we seem to be treating animals as a kind of last resort. Frequently, and paradoxically, they are seen to embody everything we find loathsome, repugnant or unworthy in our own species. A sadistic rapist will be described as 'bestial'. The unfortunate individual born with gross facial deformity was quickly dubbed 'the Elephant Man'.

History supplies us with a vast number of unflattering references to people with what were seriously believed to be animal-like traits. The poet John Milton compared his enemies to 'owls, cuckoos, asses, apes and dogs'; Karl Marx called Malthus a 'baboon'; while the Quaker George Fox in the 17th century recorded that some of his contemporaries thought that women had 'no souls, no more than a goose'.

Putting animals in their rightful place

In the light of this long tradition of ambiguous attitudes towards animals, it is easy to see why Charles Darwin became extremely unpopular among many contemporaries when he not only reminded them that we too are 'animals' but – horror of horrors – members of a very extended animal family, with fairly close relatives among the apes (notably chimpanzees) and monkeys. Satirists and cartoonists had a field-day relating Darwin himself to the monkeys, proving, naturally, the inherent stupidity of the father of evolutionary theory. But the argument was not so much a scientific as a philosophical controversy. What was at stake was a belief. The world, according to the powerful Creationist lobby, was created about 6000 years ago, with millions of plants and animal species *in situ*, all laid out according to a great Master Plan devised by the Almighty Architect. Among them was *Homo sapiens* – 'Wise Man' – the pinnacle of the natural world. How absurd, then, to suggest, as Darwin and the evolutionists did, that we had not always been as we are, but that, in common with all other species, we had changed gradually, over many millions of years, into what we are from something else, a form akin to related species living in trees and consuming nuts and bananas!

Weightlifters of the forest floor, unite! Like bees, the leaf-cutting ants of Central America form working colonies, here carrying leaves many times their size back to the nest.

With the passage of time, most people have come to accept the initially disconcerting idea of man as a 'naked ape'. To many it now seems incontrovertible. But it is salutary, since it is consistent with some of the trends already noted in our historic relationship with animals, to remember that there are still plenty of Creationists around. Some are old-style Biblical fundamentalists who simply uphold the concept of a static Creation with the in-built, traditional superiority of our species over others. Others concede that evolution may well occur but not in our species. Toads, albatrosses, sharks and lemurs may well evolve under the pressures of natural selection. But not ourselves. We are different. Unique.

Why is this so? Well, the argument runs, our evolutionary history must differ from that of other species simply because we have features that no other animals possess. We have high intelligence, an artistic sense, social subtlety, technological skills, possibly an immortal soul (unlike the deprived goose!) and, most conspicuous of all, language. Chimps can click, chatter and grimace, horses bellow, birds twitter and dogs bark. But we can talk in a variety of languages and accents, compose and read sonnets, learn lines for a play and tell a garage mechanic what is wrong with the car. Animals do not possess anything like these human skills, least of all in communication. Or do they?

A workers' collective: honeybees swarming in an elder bush. Such high levels of social cohesion would be impossible without an enormous amount of bee-to-bee communication.

Seek and ye shall find

By shifting our perspective away from the human-centred to a broadly comparative approach, we begin to see how short-sighted this kind of reasoning really is. Increasingly we are discovering that what we have tended to regard as unique to our species is far from being so. Features that we cherish as quintessentially human can turn out even to be quite commonplace in the animal world, provided we look for them in the right places and in the right way.

Let us consider, for a start, the whole matter of animal communication and animal language. Our rich literary heritage surely justifies our belief in the supremacy of human language. It is without doubt an incomparably rich instrument of superlative expressiveness and subtlety. But beware the trap of biological parochialism. Look around the animal kingdom a little and you will find some quite extraordinary linguistic attributes. The so-called 'social insects', such as ants and bees, must have a highly efficient communication system to maintain their astonishingly coherent societies. Insects employ a range of chemicals as message carriers and use other biological signalling devices to keep in contact while working together, to warn one another of the approach of predators, to indicate the precise location of food sources and to organize their sexual activities to maximum effect.

It would be irrelevant to point out that bees do not write novels or that termites do not form fringe theatre groups, and that consequently they must operate at an inferior linguistic level to us. No human communication system has ever bettered the one which ensures the social coherence of ants ferrying supplies to the nest with the mechanical precision of the finest Swiss watch. Where can you see a mass of human individuals exhibiting the totally harmonious behaviour of a swarm of bees or a shoal of fish? This collective effort is sustained by communication, the subtleties of which we are only now beginning to document and appreciate.

Birds employ a wide variety of different kinds of vocalization, each specialized in function and purpose. They even have regional accents, and can give out false alarm calls, as when one member of the flock sends a signal to the rest to scatter even though there is no predator around; a bird, in short, that cries 'wolf', but never too often.

√ Large-brained creatures such as chimps and dolphins are so adept at communicating with each other that we can still only speculate at their potential level of expression. The rapid clicks and whistles of the dolphin may represent a language not unlike ours, with words, grammar, dialect and so on. As a matter of fact, some human languages incorporate throaty clicks in their vocabulary, so that even the superficial differences between human and dolphin languages are not as wide as they first appear. Interpretation of the dolphin's 'speech' nevertheless represents a challenge even more formidable, say, than that facing an explorer coming upon an unknown tribe in a dense tropical rain forest. But in theory it can and doubtless will be done. We shall be returning to this subject later, together with the related issue of the extent to which we can teach our ways of communication to another species with its own complex language. Can our primate relatives, for example, learn to speak, using human symbols?

If we are not unique in our use of language, however one chooses to define the term (no easy task), neither are we in our deployment of technology to achieve our ends. Far from it. The more we look at the natural world, the longer grows the list of apparently man-made devices where

In for the kill. Having precisely located a moth using its sensitive echo-location system, the greater horseshoe bat homes in on its prey.

'nature got there first'. Tools, pesticides, electric shock repellants, structural engineering, laser guns – these are just a handful of the technologies we have been handling for at most a few thousand years while nature has known them all for millions of years. Nowhere so much, perhaps, as in warfare. The Wooden Horse of Troy has a natural counterpart, as does the rocket launcher. Both the underwater echo-location device and the aerial radar system were anticipated by animals. The bat uses a rapid scan of high-frequency sound waves to detect prey and predators at night, bouncing the sound it has generated off any obstacles, and from the returning signal calculating precisely their range and bearing. Quite recently it has been discovered that rats do something similar. They emit tiny whistles, again for echo-location purposes, rather like a blind person tapping a stick or even emitting a whistle to establish the position of furniture in a room. So the world's first precision acoustic engineers are to be found perching on barns and living in sewers.

There are literally thousands of ways in which animals' communicational abilities and the behaviour these govern resemble those of humans. In this book we shall be looking in detail at these analogies and asking just how far we can – or should – push the comparisons. Would we for instance be justified in crediting the echo-locating bat or dolphin with 'intelligence' or 'consciousness' (again a tricky term to define) because it acts in a calculating manner? Or do we reserve these attributes solely for humans? If so, how about our family dog? It has an acute sense of smell, vastly more sensitive than ours, which it uses to read complex signals left as chemicals in the deposits of other dogs. It could be argued that this is not just animal efficiency but shrewdness that almost verges on the uncanny.

Were we to look upon other animals, say, as alien species of another planet we might well conclude that some are indeed intelligent. Astronomers are engaged in a long-term project called SETI – the Search for Extraterrestrial Intelligence – whereby powerful radio telescopes are used to listen for signs of intelligent life elsewhere in the Universe. What they are seeking are patterns of sounds rather than random noises, structure as opposed to chaos. Only then will they infer that some far-distant beings are sending messages. Yet with the dog and its immense range of chemical scents, or even the squid with its myriad colour and pattern combinations (now known to be associated with squid-to-squid messages), perhaps we already have examples of Earth-bound intelligence, in the broadest sense of the term, that could much more quickly and easily be investigated.

To do so effectively we need to jettison the age-old attitudes that have blinkered us in the past. It has suited us, from a position of ignorance, to think of the 'lower orders' of the animal kingdom as the below-stairs organisms, acting simply on the blind dictates of evolutionary pressures – finding food, searching for a mate, securing shelter. Current research into animal consciousness upsets this tidy world view in no uncertain terms.

By revising our attitudes we can perhaps begin to appreciate the message of the ecologists who for some time have been reminding us that humans and animals live not in the opposing camps of servant and master, but in symbiosis in a common environment. Understanding the communicational skills of animals, therefore, does not merely have curiosity value but is of genuine ecological importance. It would be a route towards preserving our precious planet.

In the rest of the book we shall be discovering what steps have already been taken to this end.

Chapter Three

Varieties of Communication

As a starting point let us take a walk through any forest, woodland or jungle. Immediately we are confronted with a veritable Babel of familiar animal languages. Clicks, buzzes, shrieks, whistles, croaks, and cawing form part of the very fabric of the environment: and these are just those forms of communication that we can hear for ourselves. There are many more that we cannot pick up nearly so readily.

We are in the position of someone bound for abroad, with only a smattering of a foreign language. Our modest linguistic resources will serve us quite well for straightforward operations such as paying for food at a supermarket checkout or asking the way to the museum or police station. But when we want to go beyond this and exchange more subtle forms of information, to converse, say, on politics, art or science, our command of the language does not go far enough. So, too, when we want to tune into the languages of animals. Our speech, with its associated facial and bodily expressions, may provide us with all we require to communicate with one another. In the foreign territory of other species, however, we need to broaden our range considerably.

The difficulties are, in fact, enormous. Biologists studying all kinds of living creatures, from the most primitive to the most complex, do not totally agree as to what constitutes 'communication' in the first place. Suppose we start by defining it as 'the transmission of information from animal A to animal B in such a way that the former influences the behaviour of the latter'. So when a mouse scampering around in a farmyard leaves a scent acting as a sexual attractant that is detected by another mouse, we can safely say that mouse A is 'communicating' with mouse B.

But what if the rustling in the grass of that same mouse is detected by a hungry owl which, having got the 'message', swoops down for the kill? Communication between mouse and predator? If not, why not? Without getting too embroiled in the subtle arguments that biologists love to indulge in on this very fundamental point, we can perhaps draw the line at the notion that one characteristic of communication is that the sender of the signal usually benefits from the resultant action. Otherwise evolution would have acted in such a way as to select out that particular characteristic. In other words, there is what one might call an element of evolutionary advantage in the message. The mouse 'intends' to leave a trail to attract a mate, but not to get itself eaten.

Even in this limited sense, however, there is clearly an immense problem in trying to understand the languages of animals that differ so radically from ourselves. The unaccustomed linguistic techniques, the unfamiliar vocabulary, grammar, accents and gestures, are completely alien to human eyes, ears and noses. If we do manage to detect and recognize certain signals

– whether they involve sound, vision, smell, touch or taste – we have to interpret them and try to determine what such a message means for the animal concerned.

This may seem an impossible task but scarcely a week seems to pass without some researcher, somewhere, managing to add yet another exotic animal language to the enormously varied compendium of non-human communication channels.

Articulate insects

We can, for example, see powerful forms of communication at work among insects, often mistakenly thought of as unsubtle organisms with little to say to one another. This is patently untrue. Insects are among the most communicative of all creatures, though we cannot begin to appreciate the extent, simply because of the sheer numbers of insect species that teem over our planet. The eminent biologist Edward O. Wilson puts it in perspective when he states: 'There are more species of ants in a square kilometre of Brazilian forest than all the species of primates in the world, more workers in a single colony of driver ants than all the lions and elephants in Africa.'

Researchers are busy investigating the manner in which these vast colonies of social insects, such as ants, termites and bees, manage to cohere. In other words, what channels of communication enable them to operate in such immense numbers, constantly in contact with one another, their actions

Termite talk: in colonies numbering up to 2 million, much of the information exchanged between members is in the form of chemical secretions.

Inadvertent communication? A tawny owl swoops to take a wood mouse betraying its presence by rustling the undergrowth.

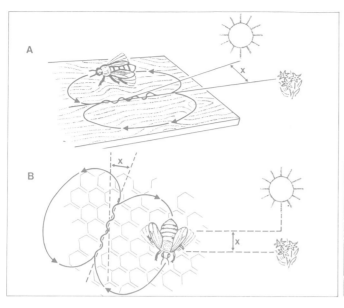

perfectly coordinated? Take the honeybee, a social insect *par excellence*. An individual worker bee will leave the hive in search of food. Once it has located a suitable source, itself a complex procedure, it returns to the fold and passes on information about the precise location of the chosen flowers to its fellow bees. The way it does this has fascinated generations of observers, including Dr James Gould of Princeton University, who has made a special study of the linguistic skills of bees, alongside their many other accomplishments.

The honeybee conveys information through its distinctive dances, of which there are two types. One is the 'round' dance whereby a worker bee which has located food less than some 50 yards from the hive simply rushes around in circles. This activity appears to attract the attention of the other bees which then pick up traces of flower odour from the food-finder, and fly off for a meal. The second dance, the exotic 'waggle', is a more subtle, complex means of communication.

The waggle dance occurs when the food source is at greater distances; and according to James Gould's painstaking research, it shows the bee using body movements in much the same way as humans use words, that is with symbolic, representational content. The bee often performs this dance on the vertical plane of the honeycomb within the hive. Its movement across the comb consists of a straight run interspersed with emphatic side-to-side shakes of the body and accompanied by bursts of sound. The line and duration of this run contain much vital information. The angle between the central axis of the dance and the vertical plane is exactly the same as the angle between the path to the food source and the sun. So the bee is passing on to its colleagues a kind of ritualized, geometrically based map to help them find their way. Remarkably, they can understand the waggled guidance instruction, which evidently provides information both on direction and distance, enabling them to reach the food.

A further intriguing feature of the bee's waggle dance is how the other workers in the hive actually perceive the messages it contains. Another biologist at Princeton, William Towne, has studied this aspect in several species of Asian honeybee, working from the premiss that a variety of options

(*Above left*) The honeybee's waggle dance is a symbolic language based on the fact that bees use the sun to navigate themselves to distant food sources. Fig A shows how the alignment of a dance on a horizontal plane would provide the necessary flight information to others. They need to fly at angle X to the sun to reach the food. However, the dance is often performed on a honeycomb which lies on a *vertical* plane (Fig B). Therefore the dancer aligns its movements at an angle to the vertical which is exactly the same as angle X on the horizontal plane.

(*Above right*) The waggle dance of a worker honeybee, surrounded by other prospective food gatherers.

might be at the disposal of the hive members: feeling the waggler's body movements, sensing the movement of air produced by the dance and receiving signals from the sounds emitted during the dance.

It turns out that different species have different ways of getting the message. Some learn about the location of the food source purely visually, forming a circle and watching the performer; some receive tactile signals, interpreting location data by touching the waggler's body; and others seem to get their information by a combination of acoustic and tactile means, according to whether or not they live in dark cavities where visual signalling alone would be inappropriate. But the manner in which these sound cues are perceived, and the precise roles of visual or tactile cues, are still open questions.

In addition to employing a variety of methods for transmitting and receiving information, bees also appear to possess what can best be described as regional dialects. Just as human body gestures can have different meanings in different countries, so, too, do those of bees. When an Austrian bee, for example, waggles its body for a certain length of time this means that food is 50 yards away. One waggle in Egypt, however, signifies only 10 yards!

Meaningful molecules in the air

The language of dance with its associated buzzing, as demonstrated by the bee, represents only a minute fraction of the insect communications repertoire. There are many more ways of making contact. Whereas some insects are cartographers, others are biochemists, capable of transmitting signals by substances known as 'pheromones'. Pheromones are naturally occurring chemicals secreted by one member of a species to influence the behaviour of another. These powerful molecules, which are used, incidentally, by all kinds of animals, not just insects (and perhaps even humans), have several important advantages over other channels of communication. They can, for example, be employed in situations where auditory or visual signals are either absent or difficult to discern, as when the creature is near to a loud source of sound or during the night. What is more, pheromones can remain in the environment for a long time without jeopardizing the safety of the individual sender. They can also travel through the atmosphere over surprisingly long distances, so that sender and receiver need not be as close together physically as might be necessary for the exchange, say, of a visual signal.

Pheromones seem to be deployed primarily as sexual attractants in the unending search for a suitable mate: nature's own aftershaves and toilet waters. But they can convey other types of message. One species of ant we shall be encountering later, for instance, acts as a recruiting sergeant, using a 'propaganda' pheromone to enlist help. In fact, it has even been suggested by Dr David Rhoades that not only animate organisms but inanimate trees too may utilize these substances as alarm calls. Some trees, when attacked by insect predators, secrete toxic chemicals in order to ward off the aggressor. Dr Rhoades discovered that a tree assailed by pests in one part of a forest not only generated its own defence chemicals but appeared to send some kind of warning message to other trees in the area, because the latter immediately emitted their toxins even though they were not actually being attacked at the time! Having established that there was no root-to-root communication between the trees, Dr Rhoades inclines to the view that an alarm pheromone must be in operation.

True or not, one can easily see the advantage of knowing more about the pheromonal language of animals, especially those that are a nuisance to farmers and crop growers. If we could discover more about the chemical attractant and alarm systems of plant pests, it might be possible to devise ways of trapping or otherwise controlling them naturally, instead of having to spray insecticides hopefully in buckshot fashion over wide tracts of countryside.

We could, for example, borrow the pheromonal language of the species of wild potato that secretes an alarm chemical to ward off aphids. And perhaps future generations of rose growers will be fighting greenfly and blackfly by scaring them off in their own, species-specific language rather than trying to spray them to death. There could be enormous economic advantages in our acquiring this subtle chemical language.

It is a sobering thought that in America one species of moth whose caterpillar has a liking for corn and cotton plants costs the agricultural industry a cool $700 million a year in pesticides alone. At the State University of New York, Professor Glenn Prestwich is working on a way to reduce the bill by branching into the insects' pheromonal system. His idea is to use the insects' own chemical for what he terms 'mating disruption'. If the pheromone were to be put out in dispensers around a corn or cotton field, the whole field would, so far as the male moth is concerned, smell like a female. 'In that case,' says Professor Prestwich, 'a single female producing a small amount of pheromone can't compete with all of these plastic things smelling like females, and so the male ends up looking around and not finding anything.' In fact, in an estimated 95–98% of cases the male fails to mate as

A plague of migrating locusts wiping out a farmer's crop in southern Africa. In future, locust populations may be controlled by pheromonal means, tapping in to the insect's own communication system to limit its breeding.

he would have done before disruption. Family planning, then, on a gigantic scale.

There are a few practical disadvantages to this technique, so Glenn Prestwich plans to go one stage further. He is working on the design of special molecules that will act as 'chemical scalpels', effectively excising the highly sensitive odour receptor cells in the offending moth. Once the receptors are inactivated, the male is rendered totally insensitive to the female's charms. 'It's essentially,' says Prestwich, 'a chemical odour blindness.'

Choirs and instrumentalists

The communicative abilities of insects are still far from exhausted. In addition to dances and pheromones, they can also command an impressively wide range of sounds, tailored to their purposes. The male cicada has a song that can be heard as far as half a mile away; the individual is then joined by an entire chorus, synchronized with a precision to rival that of any opera company. The female cicada, too, has a ticking song which she uses to good effect to attract a mate. Indeed, like some insect Carmen clacking her castanets, she can grab the attention of males simply by a flick of the wing. Each tick of the wing encourages the males to advance. When she stops her ticking, the males come to a halt. Incidentally, there are some 1500 known species of cicada, each with its specific language based on the amplitude of the ticks and their pattern of delivery.

Species recognition is important, too, for crickets and grasshoppers which generate their distinctive sounds respectively by rubbing their two wings together or rubbing their hindlegs against their wings. To us these songs may seem much the same wherever and whenever we hear them, but to different species of cricket and grasshopper they vary as much as English does from Chinese. By recording and analyzing these insect sounds, researchers have been able to identify all kinds of species-specific patterns. They have also identified different types of song: some for establishing territory by the male, some for attracting a female; songs of courtship and arousal, produced by a change in frequency of the notes emitted; and, inevitably, sounds of aggression if another male tries to muscle in on a chosen partner.

Biologists have long wondered what precisely prompts an insect such as the cricket to begin singing. And, once started, why does it stop? Consider, however, that although the male may hope to attract the attentions of a passing female by its song, he pays a price for it in terms of energy consumption. Singing depletes natural fuel, so there must come a point when the cricket decides to call a halt and try again later when the batteries are recharged. So we are not the only creatures who need to know when to hold our tongue.

To the familiar sounds of the cricket, as well as the many well-documented hisses, chirps, clicks, whistles and buzzes of other insects, researchers are regularly adding newly discovered variations. In addition to the low-frequency signals produced by the vibrating wings of the fruit fly *Drosophila*, they have, for example, identified a form of semaphore. The Japanese species of the insect appears to use its black wing tips as a visual signal, rather like coloured flags employed at sea for sending messages from ship to ship. This is not surprising when we consider the frequent use of natural semaphore by other species, such as the male firefly which aims its unmistakable luminescent pulses at females as they sit in the foliage at night.

What is perhaps remarkable is that in the case of the firefly, a relatively lowly species in the natural hierarchy of living organisms, the flashing constitutes what might be termed the application of technology. On-off light sources are here employed for message transmission just as we might use intermittent sound sources in the form of Morse code.

Communications technology, if we can call it that, is not proving to be all that rare in the insect kingdom. Scientists are at present getting very interested in the apparent sensitivity of crickets, termites, beetles and moths to electrical and magnetic fields. They believe that certain species may be exploiting electricity and magnetism through specialized sensory cells as a means of communication, which is tantamount to suggesting that they have evolved the equivalent of tiny telephone-like instruments for relaying information by electromagnetic means. Alexander Graham Bell, therefore, was beaten to it. Even the burglar alarm has an animal counterpart, this time among a species of spider which, unlike most, lives in colonies. The colony builds a colective web so designed that whenever a prey insect lands on it the threads relay the intruder's buzzing to the waiting spider. But it is an alarm with a slight refinement. The web can discriminate between the vibrations of a prey and those of other spiders in the colony. That dispenses with the tiresome business of false alarms that bedevil our domestic systems.

Water talk

Animals succeed in speaking to one another whatever the medium they inhabit. Not only do frogs and toads converse obviously and vocally across a pond or lake; the fish beneath the surface also manage to communicate freely. Indeed, water is a better medium for transmission than is commonly realized, at least so far as acoustic signals are concerned. Optically, water offers only a poor channel, diffusing and distorting visual information; but noises carry extremely well, as several hundred species of sound-emitting fish will testify.

Fish give out a wide range of calls in several ways: rubbing together teeth or spines, changing speed or direction to affect the flow of water, and using their swim bladder as a resonating chamber controlled by muscle action. They appear to emit their calls when on the move, suggesting perhaps that sound may be important in helping maintain the cohesion of a school, which can comprise a few to millions of individuals. But sometimes grouping has its drawbacks. The swimming sounds made by a school of tasty anchovy will inadvertently signal their presence to marauding jacks, but in return they will be unable to detect the moving predators.

We too could probably profit from knowing more about the languages of fish. After all, human fishermen are also in the business of locating large shoals of eatable wildlife, so there could be some economic advantage in an ability to eavesdrop on our aquatic relatives. Indeed, this has already been done in the case of the North Sea haddock. Dr Anthony Hawkins, using hydrophones dropped into the water, has actually detected and recorded haddock 'conversations'. They consist of various sonic emissions in the guise of single or repeated knocks and grunts, the former mainly during shows of male aggression, the latter as defensive or escape sounds. The really interesting part of the haddock vocabulary, however, occurs during mating and spawning. By breeding the fish in a large tank, it has been possible to record a characteristic sequence of courtship sounds. The male begins the process with aggressive knocking calls, thereby establishing his sexual sway over a

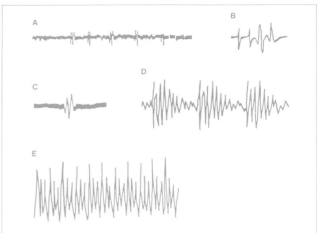

(*Above left*) From the sea to the dinner table. Huge shoals of whitebait may, like the haddock, be located by fishermen monitoring their underwater communication.

(*Above right*) Knocks, grunts and hums: calls of the male haddock as recorded on a sonogram. The precise 'meaning' of all these calls is yet to be established, but generally speaking the more aggressive the male the faster its rate of delivery.
A: A five-knock call.
B: A single-knock call.
C: A single-grunt call.
D: Rapid knocking in courtship. E: Humming call as male flaunts a female.

chosen female. As he swims round her, the knocking sounds gradually speed up and their frequency becomes higher, until they reach the level of an excited purring. This seems to have a marked triggering effect on the physiological responses of the female who begins to spawn her 10,000 or so eggs, all the while remaining curiously silent as she floats to the surface locked in a quiet embrace with her partner.

In addition to the calls of haddock, the sounds made by other economically useful fish, such as cod and Atlantic salmon, have been investigated, holding out the prospect of our acquiring a full vocabulary of fish courtship. This could be valuable in controlling the mating and spawning activities of species that hitherto have virtually escaped the attentions of fishermen. We may even learn to orchestrate the mating of fish to our own ends, manipulating them through the language they understand best: their own.

Birdsong and birdtalk

It is said that a mother in a maternity hospital can single out the individual cry of her newborn child at night, and happily sleep on when someone else's baby is screaming. Something similar is found among birds, creatures with a wide and varied acoustic repertoire. In a huge colony of clifftop gannets, the squawk of one bird will be picked out by its partner in the nest, even though it is blended with a cacophony of other cries mingling on the wind. Likewise, young guillemots will pay attention to their own parents and no others.

Birds use songs and calls in every sort of situation: the newborn chick cries to demand food; the male asserts superiority through song when he invades or tries to hold on to territory; and the all-important activities of sexual pairing, mate selection and courtship depend greatly on vocalization. Bird sounds fall broadly into two categories. There are relatively simple 'calls', consisting of just one or a few isolated bursts which convey such information as 'Danger' or 'Send help', or serve to control the movement of the flock or indicate the whereabouts of food. Then there are songs proper, longer and more complex sequences that seem to be used primarily in the breeding season, usually by the male.

By using recording equipment in the field and subjecting these tapes to computer analysis and sonagraph display, researchers have been able to compile a veritable grammar book of many avian sounds. They have acquired much revealing data concerning the situations in which these calls or songs are deployed; they have listened in to two-way 'conversations'; and, by playing back sounds to the species that made them, they have studied the precise behavioural effects of these vocalizations in the wild.

When, for instance, small garden birds 'mob' a perched owl not busy hunting at that particular time, they emit a loud click-like sound which gives a clear indication to others of the direction and location of the owl. If, however, the predator should be flying overhead, the potential prey bird will rush to cover in the nearest bush and give a halting, start-stop sort of call, so alerting others of the flock, which do the same. This type of call, unlike the mobbing click, is extremely difficult to locate with any precision. Thus the bird raises the alarm without risking detection by the predator.

Researchers have found even more intriguing kinds of variation, including the bird equivalent to human regional dialects. The celebrated biologist Peter Marler, of Rockefeller University, New York, has elaborated some provocative ideas about the songs of various sparrow species, especially the white-crowned sparrow of California. Marler puts forward the concept of a so-called 'neural template'. This means, basically, that the infant bird comes into the world not with a fully blown song readily at its disposal but just with a rough outline which it gradually perfects through hearing the song of other birds. So the sparrow accepts the songs of other members of its own species as a model for improving on its original template or outline. Furthermore, it shows a tireless capacity for memorizing such models when young, using a strategy that seems similar to the one we ourselves employ in learning to speak. The sparrow appears to memorize a song, break it up into its component parts and re-use them in an expressive, creative manner. Just as we learn words and syntax, so birds pick up bits of their language as they go along, utilizing them as and when occasion demands. And again, as with us, there are regional variations: dialects and accents, according to the models on which the growing bird is basing its repertoire. Peter Marler's findings open up some exciting avenues concerning the whole question of how animals learn their languages. It is an issue we shall return to later.

Meanwhile, other researchers such as Jack Hailman and his colleagues

(*Overleaf*) Depths of meaning: in sight of Mount Kilimanjaro a family group of elephants in Amboseli National Park communicates using low-frequency rumbles.

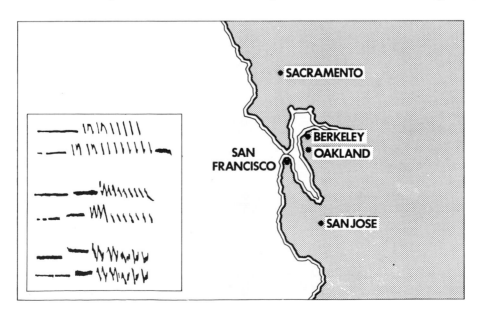

Birdsong dialects in the San Francisco Bay area. Researchers have identified three distinct songs of the white-crowned sparrow, as represented in the sonograms. These correspond to residency around the Berkeley area to the north or south of San Francisco. The basic song is simple – an alerting buzz, followed by a trill. But the area variants are quite pronounced.

Millicent and Robert Ficken, at the University of Wisconsin, have been pushing the comparison between bird and human language even further. Their chosen species is *Parus atricapillus*, better known as the black-capped chickadee. The 'chick-a-dee' calls of the bird, raised usually when alarmed, were examined by means of a sound spectrograph, and subjected to various mathematical analytical techniques. Hailman and his associates found that the bird's calls could be quite closely compared to written English in exhibiting a number of important structural features apparently very similar to human language. The chickadee evidently has the ability to use a little dictionary of 'words' or note types, which it combines and recombines to form 'sentences'. In other words, from a number of basic units, comprising only four note types, it can generate a wider range of expression. In a sample of 3479 recorded calls, 362 different call types were identified, each call being capable of encoding information much like that of an isolated English word. Although, say the researchers, there are important differences between bird and human language, they find 'the avian calling system ... more language-like than any known animal communication system'.

One other obvious comparison we might make is between birdsong and human music. After all, the nightingale or the lark produce sounds that are aesthetically pleasing to us, and delivered with the flourish of an instrumental virtuoso. And music, too, is a 'language', built up of notes (the words), formed into melodies (the sentences) and according to the grammatical disciplines of harmony and key signatures. Like spoken language, music is a form of expression; and similarly it can be in turn simple or complex, unassuming or monumental, sensuous or clinical.

How far, then, can we compare the two forms? Birdsong sounds beautiful to us, but is it aesthetically pleasing for the bird? One of the great pioneers of comparative studies of humans and animals, Professor W. H. Thorpe of Cambridge University, believed that there is quite serious argument for something like musical appreciation, 'albeit on an elementary scale', existing among a number of bird species. If you listen to recordings of a blackbird throughout its singing season, you can detect certain qualitative changes, variations in the degree of musicality. During the reproductive period the male bird, intent on securing territory and finding a mate, has what Professor Thorpe called a 'functional' song – a plain version of its score. Later on, however, when its needs are secured, the blackbird – once called the Beethoven of songbirds – introduces all kinds of subtle and colourful organizational modifications, 'in a manner,' argued Professor Thorpe, 'so closely resembling our own ideas of musical form that it is difficult to deny that it is musically improved.'

Communication among mammals

For all the musicality or 'verbal' facility of birds, however, the really significant similarities in communication strategies between human and animal are probably to be found in the most highly evolved class of creatures, of which we form one species: the mammals. If we represent the 4½ billion years since the formation of the Earth to the present day by one year of 365 days, then the mammals only begin to figure prominently around 28 December; and only in the evening of 31 December do our ape-like ancestors appear – about 3 million years ago. Together with other larger mammals, therefore, we are comparative latecomers in the family of animals.

In many respects we and our close relatives, the monkeys and apes, known collectively as 'primates' (on the supercilious assumption that because humans are included, the order must be 'first' in the natural hierarchy) are inferior creatures. The mouse or dog can outsmell us, the antelope or cheetah outpaces us, the sailfish leaves us gasping in the water, and any number of 'lesser' organisms show up our inadequacies in seeing, hearing, pulling or leaping. But, of course, in one respect evolution has endowed us with a feature of enviable advantage: our large brain. And since the nervous system is ultimately the source of all activity, including communication, the tendency to explore the common ground between our language and that of the other large-brained creatures which in so many ways resemble us, is irresistible.

Yet again this is not easy. Once more we are faced with an apparent babble of meaningless grunts, roars, squeaks and chatterings from the mouths of chimps, gorillas and monkeys. A great deal of painstaking and often frustrating investigation is needed to decipher these signals in the first place, let alone establish to what extent, if any, they represent a meaningful, symbolic language of the kind that we employ.

Among the researchers to address this question has been Robert Sey-farth, who has specialized particularly in the natural vocalizations of the vervet monkeys of East Africa. Over the years Seyfarth, along with other pioneers in the field such as his wife and colleague Dorothy Cheney, has catalogued the various calls of monkeys in different contexts, trying thereby to place the sounds in their true behavioural setting. He has also been studying these vocalizations by using the 'playback' technique we have seen applied to birds: rather than relying on his own judgment as to which calls are similar or different, he has been playing them back in recorded form to the species concerned in order to determine how they are perceived by the monkeys themselves.

'Results of this work,' writes Seyfarth, 'do not indicate that non-human primates possess language. Results do, however, reveal greater complexity than previously imagined, and suggest some similarities between the function of vocalizations in the daily lives of primates and the simplest use of words by humans.' According to Peter Marler, the vocalizations of macaques or vervets are ancestral to human speech. 'Human language,' he argues, 'probably developed from the graded vocal signals of such monkeys.'

In addition to monkey alarm calls, a variety of other sounds have been documented, together with their behavioural contexts, as when a male approaches another dominant animal or watches another monkey initiate group movement. This 'vocabulary' has been transcribed into sound spectrographs, providing a picture dictionary of the vervet's repertoire. What Seyfarth and others are now asking is whether, in the everyday use of these sounds by monkeys, we can distinguish even more pronounced human characteristics. Is there, for instance, any evidence that non-human primates combine their signals to form new utterances? If so, are there any grammatical rules that govern such combinations? Secondly, is there any evidence, as we have seen in birds, of linguistic development whereby an animal seems to learn to modify its vocalizations with age?

Nature and nurture in the wild

By raising this last question, Robert Seyfarth is confronting us with a problem that psychologists of human behaviour have long been debating. It is the thorny matter of nature *versus* nurture. How far are the skills, aptitudes and accomplishments that we possess the outcome of genetic inheritance from our parents and how far shaped by our upbringing and environment? The process is undoubtedly interactive. We come into the world with a fixed genetic endowment which gives us inclinations and propensities; but we are enormously influenced by our environment as to whether we develop in one direction or another. Thus we all have a brain capable of acquiring the subtleties of language. But if two identical twins, born with exactly the same genetic endowment, were raised in two totally different contexts, the first, say, in a household where mother, father, aunts and uncles are all highly verbal individuals (poets, novelists, journalists, etc.), and the second in a completely non-bookish, non-verbal environment, the two individuals would undoubtedly display pronounced differences in verbal skills later in life.

To what extent is the same process at work among other animals so far as communication skills are concerned? There is, as we have seen, some evidence to suggest that birds build on their pre-programmed basic songs with variations learned from companions in the flock. Is the same true of other species? Does the spider, an unexpectedly proficient instrumentalist which issues vibratory signals from a file and tooth system located just below the mouth, progressively learn its repertoire by stages? Does the baby humpback whale come into the world complete with a full range of eloquently sonorous calls at its disposal?

The exact nature of the animal communications repertoire, how it is acquired and whether it is a gradual process, is still the subject of intensive research. Although these are as yet fairly open questions, already there is enough data to suggest some intriguing man-animal parallels in the language learning process. Perhaps the most powerful argument of all comes from the primates, especially chimpanzees which have been taught to use some of the gestural vocabulary of American Sign Language to 'express' themselves. The celebrated Washoe, a character we shall be looking at in more detail later in this book, under the guidance of Allen and Beatrice Gardner of the University of Nevada, stirred up a hot scientific controversy by demonstrating apparently quite garrulous skill with ASL. Washoe has, it seems, not only learned to sign for individual items such as 'drink' or 'food', but may also have acquired the capability of combining words to produce fresh concepts. When a mealtime alarm clock went off, she immediately came out with a combination of 'listen-eat' signs. It is only the human equivalent of baby talk but perhaps Washoe and other trained chimps can and will mature linguistically as they become older.

If so, could these articulate apes pass on their human-like language to other monkeys, thus producing a whole population of foreign language speakers? This may sound far-fetched until you remember the classic case of a female macaque monkey called Imo, something of a genius in the monkey world. In 1953, on the Japanese island of Koshima, she devised a method of cleaning bitter sand off the sweet potatoes she found lying on the beach, which had been dropped there deliberately by a team of scientists studying the primates. Imo simply dipped the potatoes in the water and brushed off the unpalatable particles. In the following two years, Imo's newly displayed skill spread to 90% of the other macaques in the troop. The very young, however, failed to acquire it; nor did the very old who, like fixed-in-their-ways humans, doggedly refused to follow suit.

In fact the macaques began to pick up a few other unusual skills, learning to swim and dive, and even, in the case of one of the troop, swimming to a neighbouring island. In a short bound, then, the adaptable macaques had become maritime explorers as well. Something similar happened in Britain after the first blue tit learned to extend its natural bark-peeling behaviour to opening the tops of milk bottles left outside on a house doorstep. Once this clever tit had acquired the bottle-opening craft, its companions throughout the land quickly caught on, much to the dismay of milk buyers everywhere.

Thus learning among animals, especially primates, can be a rapid and powerful force, just as it is among humans. If linguistic skills could be similarly transmitted, we might see genuinely creative, even artistic, communication between other species. It has been said that, simply by hitting the keys of a typewriter at random, a million monkeys in many millions of years could reproduce the works of Shakespeare. Perhaps, though, it need not be quite so much a matter of chance. The assorted grunts and squeaks of tree-dwelling monkeys may seem, and indeed are, far removed from the sublimities of a sonnet. Yet a monkey that uses manual skills strategically to improve the quality of its food or who manipulates a sign language for the deaf to its own ends is a long way from being simply a quasi-instinctive animal with little natural capacity for self improvement. Learning, whether from teachers, parents, books or films, can go a long way. Who knows what communication skills are yet to be developed and refined by our primate-relatives?

A thirst for knowledge. The blue tits of Britain have quickly learned how to make an easy living in a man-made environment.

Play and the young animal

Play is a serious business. Watch a group of youngsters in a play-school. They are not just having a game but learning, in pretend form, about life in general and social life in particular: how to interact in a group or on a one-to-one basis; how to compete – win or lose; and how to make running adjustments in their relationships as they develop. So, too, with chimps who, through their infantile and juvenile play, seem to be learning all about the behaviours, primarily of an aggressive or sexual nature, that they will need in adult life.

Jane Goodall, Robert Hinde and other primatologists have provided us with many insights into the play habits of chimpanzees, as they move about with their characteristic, ambling gait, make teeth-exposed funny faces or indulge in finger wrestling. For them play seems to be an important developmental ingredient, allowing the young animal to test itself in a harmless, self-indulgent way, broadening its behavioural repertoire and permitting it, like a human going to an avant-garde theatrical performance, to depart now and then from the norms and conventions of its immediate social group. Among chimps, too, we also see, as in human children, sex stereotyping in their forms of play. Just as little girls, as a result of their sex-stereotypical upbringing, will, broadly speaking, be less physically active, preferring quieter forms of game to rushing ferociously around the nursery, so male chimps indulge in more rough and tumble than the females.

Animals, like human children, may suffer from being deprived of normal emotional experience in the early years, especially access to a mother's love and attention. In a famous experiment with rhesus monkeys, Harry Harlow graphically showed the effects of maternal deprivation. He separated youngsters from their mothers and gave them a 'substitute' in the form of a terry-towel dummy which the infant monkeys duly hugged and cluthed incessantly. But when they were later allowed to join other monkeys, they were found to have severe behavioural problems: indeed, had they been human they would have been classified as 'psychologically disturbed', if not psychotic. The animals were in turns hyper-aggressive and autistic. They were sexually incompetent, males not knowing how to mount females and females refusing to be mounted. When 'raped' by an experienced male, females failed to bring up their resultant offspring properly. In short, among monkeys there are, as we have learned from a needlessly prolonged series of cruel deprivation experiments, precisely the same sorts of disturbances that the psychologist Dr John Bowlby has identified among human infants suffering maternal separation.

Observations of animal play (not just in primates, incidentally, but in other fun-loving creatures such as kittens) and maternal deprivation studies seem to suggest that there are many close comparisons to be made between human and animal learning and development. Just as we depend on stimulus and practice to convert our baby-talk babblings into recognizable speech, so other species likewise rely on 'models' which they can imitate. They, too, need to try out future experiences in ritual play form. How would a cat hone up its sharp predatory reflexes without going through its wool-catching phase as a kitten? The spectacle of a kitten crouching in front of a ball of wool, then suddenly leaping and scooping it up in its paws, is in its way like a four-year-old child in a Suzuki violin class, watching the teacher, imitating, reproducing and repeating, thereby acquiring that particular skill. Humans starting with the basic outlines can go on to improvise, embellish and create. Other animals can do so as well.

An unfinished catalogue

We still have a great deal to learn about the full potentiality of animal language skills. In their studies of the humpback whale, Katharine and Roger Payne found that all the animals in a group change the melodies of their songs in exactly the same way, an example of what might be called 'cultural evolution'. It was as if the whales were altering their tunes according to prevailing fashions, in much the same way as composers over the centuries have developed musical styles ranging from classicism and romanticism to twelve-tone modernism. But what of those animals whose communication channels we are only just beginning to tap? Take, for instance, the elephant, a creature which for many years was thought to vocalize only by means of familiar trumpetings and bellows? While making recordings of elephants at Washington Park Zoo in Portland, Oregon, Katharine Payne noticed unusual throbbing sensations in the air, 'like the vibrations from the lowest note on a big pipe organ, or the slight shock wave one can feel from far-off thunder' Further research revealed that the captive elephants were in fact emitting very low frequency rumbles from a spot on their forehead where the nasal passages enter the skull. No one, apart from other elephants, had ever before perceived these extremely deep sounds, which represent a further level of communication never hitherto suspected. They also show that large land mammals can produce noises well below the normal thresholds of human hearing. So how many other familiar animals might do the same? The giraffe? The horse? The cow?

We can only speculate. But of one thing we can be sure. There are many more animal languages to be discovered and catalogued. As Al Jolson put it 'You ain't heard nothin' yet!'

Play-fighting among fox cubs: all part of growing up.

Chapter Four

Living Together

The shark, in more ways than one, is an exceptional organism. Not only does this successful predator manage, for reasons not understood, to remain free from cancers, which makes it of special interest to medical scientists, the shark also possesses, along with few other animals, such as the bear, one rare ability. For the most part, it thrives not as a member of a society but as a loner.

This is decidedly unusual. The general rule in the wild is that birds of a feather, not to mention other species, be they arthropods, molluscs, fish, amphibians, mammals or insects, stick together. In fact even the solitary shark shows some signs of social behaviour: it has a variety of bodily gestures – 'shark shimmies' – to communicate dominance or to signal an imminent attack. Social behaviour prevails throughout the animal kingdom. There seems to be, with animals as with humans, a natural weighting against the lone creature. Just as we tend to aggregate and congregate for our mutual comfort, security and benefit, so too do animals in the wild.

Again we can step back down the ladder of evolution and see this principle operating in primitive organisms such as the colonial invertebrates. Corals and other primitive colonial marine organisms, the ectoprocts, for

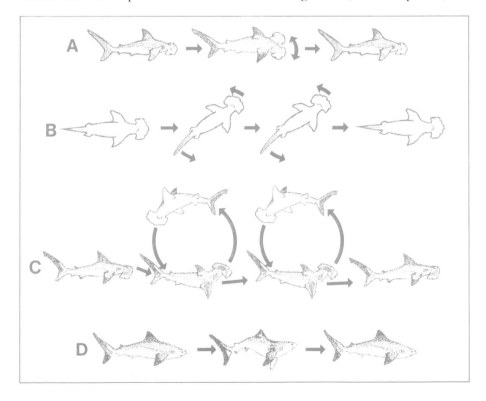

Shark shimmies. A: Subordinate hammerhead shark indicates submission by a headshake. B: The male torso thrust, exposing a white belly in order to establish dominance. C: The loop-the-loop, corkscrewing manoeuvre, again to assert superiority. D: A grey reef shark indicates aggressive intent, back hunched, snout raised and fins lowered.

example, form beautiful underwater societies where individuals totally sub-ordinate themselves to the overall group. In any given colony of ectoprocts there will be a range of functional specialists, some for defence, some for feeding, some for reproduction. Together they form a successful corporate unit in which the individual is, in the words of Edward O. Wilson, 'virtually annihilated as an entity'.

The notion has become fashionable nowadays of 'selfish genes', which we often take to mean that an individual puts his own welfare and security first. But as the corals and ectoprocts show, genes can also be considered as collective entities. In fact, there is a lot of evidence, not just among corals but in many higher animals, that an individual will often try to further the interests of others, even, apparently, at highest personal loss. Like the Kamikaze pilot who dies in a spasm of patriotic altruism, animals too may place the needs of the community above their own.

Animals, like us, form a broad spectrum of social groupings. The starling lives most of the time as an individual or as one of a pair, but will frequently participate in *ad hoc* associations as a member of a mixed-species feeding flock. The wolf and the dolphin, on the other hand, seem to spend all their lives with others of their species. Indeed, if isolated, say by being kept in captivity, both these animals show evident signs of suffering, even to the point of dying, so great is their need for company.

Even more interdependent are social insects such as ants, bees, wasps and termites, which live in colonies where every individual has a specific job to do, and cannot lead a separate existence.

Grouping has many advantages. It may literally be a matter of life or death. Waterfleas cannot live on their own in water that is highly alkaline, but they can do so if there are enough of them together, because the combined output of their respiratory products is sometimes sufficiently acidic to render the water acceptable.

A large group may also afford individuals relative protection from predators. With a number of flocking birds on the alert, an approaching fox or cat is less likely to go undetected than if a solitary prey were the target. A single alarm call is sufficient to warn the whole flock. A group can also take evasive or retaliatory action in concert, mobbing the enemy. A collection of animals can improve its chances of finding and catching prey. Furthermore, if animals stick together, they can also synchronize their reproductive cycles, reducing the breeding season, a time of high vulnerability, to a minimum and thereby limiting their availability to predators.

All for one and one for all

In order to work, a society must hang together. Unless the groupings are to be fluid, unreliable and anarchic, they need a defined structure. So deeply rooted are animal societies that they soon reassert themselves after having been artificially suppressed. This is obvious to any town dweller who has seen wild dogs – ferals – which have shaken off their relatively recent domestication to hunt in pairs and hang around the streets in packs. The feral demonstrates how easily the hearthrug dog, cosseted by its owner with canned foods and titbits, reverts to its lupine ancestry.

The ultimate reason for social coherence is the drive to survive. Rats, for instance, manage to avoid man-laid traps and poisons, having learned from past victims of their dire consequences. They then pass on this self-saving race memory to the next generations in their tight-knit clans; the young rats learn

Brown rats banqueting
on a rubbish tip.

avoidance behaviour by watching the trap-wise adults.

For rat or dog, bird or fish, vertebrate or invertebrate, collective behaviour and social cohesion imply communication between individual members. It would be impossible for a human tribe to live or hunt together
without verbal and non-verbal communication; nor could large contemporary societies function without the use of mass communications media to
spread information of common interest. It is equally unlikely that animal
societies could exist without an enormous number of signals being exchanged between individuals and groups.

A graphic illustration of this is the social communication system of the
hyena. Hyenas live in groups called clans, but not all the time. They may
forsake their close-knit communities to go off on their own or in little knots
of two or three, sometimes for long periods. Then they may return to the
larger group for a while, perhaps for hunting purposes. In order to maintain
social cohesion in the face of this come-and-go lifestyle, hyenas have evolved
an elaborate series of signals for their all-important greetings ceremonies.
After some mutual head sniffing, two hyenas stand head to tail and lift the
hind leg in order to expose their genitals for further sniffing and licking.
There is also a good deal of vocalized communication: whoops, grunts,
groans, growls, screams and squeals, not to mention complex body talk in
the form of careful tail and ear positioning.

The collective behaviour of the African naked mole rat has tempted some
researchers to point to this particular species as the zenith of mammalian
socializing, so complex are its interactions. It is, as in bee societies with their

50

central queen, a matriarchal set-up. The dominant female mole rat is the only creature which can breed, but she exercises enormous control over male and female workers in the community to ensure that all her many needs are adequately met. The workers dig tunnels and find food to carry into the nesting chamber, acting in fact, like a true proletariat, subservient to the needs of their rodent monarch.

Close-up film of these nesting complexes reveals the extent to which the constantly sniffing mole rat sees, hears and responds to the world through its nose. Indeed, the dominant female is able to wield her power by the scents which she produces. Odour provides the organizational mechanism to keep soldiers and workers in their humble place.

The sense of smell, too, can lead an animal to acts of self-sacrifice – in the case of the bee, for queen and country. If a colony is attacked by a hornet, a worker will challenge the invader and die in the unequal struggle. But there is never any shortage of other bees ready to lay down their lives in the victim's place. Superficially it looks like the ultimate example of altruism, but what really happens is that the dying bee emits a chemical which unfailingly attracts fellow bees to the scene of the carnage. They are pre-programmed just to keep on advancing under the influence of this substance: choice, either moral or political, hardly enters into it. Nevertheless this attractant does serve to unify and thus maintain the bee society. Sooner or later the cannon fodder prevail and by sheer force of numbers destroy the hornet.

The role of communication in the apparent altruism shown by another 'social' insect, the wasp, has been studied by a researcher from the Smithsonian Tropical Research Institute, Mary-Jane West-Eberhard. Many wasps, like bees, operate a caste system with a controlling queen dominating her workers, who are often near starvation. These lower orders are wholly self-effacing; they may be 'losers' but they still help to rear nestmates. Wasps, like bees, use not just chemical signals but a whole range of other communication strategies: drumming the antennae against the nest, adopting stereotyped bodily postures, exchanging food, dancing, emitting audible

Social hierarchies among hyenas are expressed in characteristic vocalizations and body language. A dominant female (right) threatens a young, submissive hyena.

alarm calls and so on. All these help to maintain social cohesion but not, says Dr West-Eberhard, because the worker is 'self-sacrificial' in the same sense as a soldier at the Front. They die for the sake of their relatives who are then able to carry on the genetic line. It is a kind of reproduction by proxy.

Obviously these channels of communication can work extraordinarily well in insect societies. Think, for instance, of a termite colony, which differs from that of the bee or ant in having both a king and queen at the top of the social scale. The queen is an astoundingly efficient egg-laying machine, able to produce anything up to 36,000 eggs in the space of 24 hours. With such a population explosion occurring daily, small wonder that termite colonies will burrow out extensive tunnels, some of them hundreds of metres long, to reach life-sustaining water sources. Only an organism that can command an extensive range of information-carrying techniques could manage such coordinated feats of civil engineering, child care, self-defence and food production. We marvel at such spectacular human feats as the construction of the Pyramids or the Golden Gate Bridge. Yet social insects are continually communicating with one another to realize equally impressive mega-projects on a routine basis. Moreover, they were making their architectural master-pieces long before our species had evolved.

Safety in numbers

A conspicuous bird is the flamingo: large, brilliantly coloured with vivid pink plumage, flocking in shallow tropical lakes and lagoons in huge colonies of up to one million members. The flamingo makes an obvious and, you would think, easy target for its arch enemy the jackal, a sleek, long-legged runner scavenging alone or in packs along the water's edge, sizing up its prey like a knowing housewife choosing the family's roasting joint. Indeed the jackal seems to have a virtual embarrassment of riches from which to select its next meal. It has, it seems, only to look, leap and be sated. And that is the trouble. In reality the jackal does not find it quite so easy to catch its prey because the flamingo, as a member of a flock, has improved its chances of escape by a matter of simple mathematics. The jackal's attentions are spread too wide. It can only take one prey at a time and when it pounces it is not sure, in the mad, scrambling melée of wings and feathers, just which bird to aim for. It often ends up diverted, and frustrated. His million-to-one exploit has come to nil.

You have seen the same thing a hundred times with neighbourhood dogs and cats chasing groups of birds pecking away contentedly in the grass, one second a tight little bunch of eatables, the next a dispersed flurry of separate entities. The logic of this in-built avian arithmetic dictates that, from a flock of say ten birds, an individual's survival rating is ten times that of a loner or, conversely, one-tenth of what it would be in a flock of 100 birds.

To keep on the right statistical track a bird or other social animal has to indulge in two-way communication. Sometimes the language employed will be fairly generalized. Some birds, for example, will belong to flocks consisting of a mixture of species, casual groupings that are detected by passing birds and joined or not, as the case may be. More often, though, flocks are composed of one species with a number of specific calls to persuade other members to join. Once the first bird has swooped down to feed, others soon follow.

As well as vocalizations, birds employ various display procedures. The long-tailed tit has a fairly unusual cooperative breeding system in which many nests are attended by one or more breeding 'helpers'. Birds visiting nests often make a conspicuous hover display close by, lasting a few seconds, just before they deliver food. According to Dr Peter Greig-Smith, working at the University of Sussex, this display seems to serve an important social function by communicating information that produces greater coordination between the activities of group members. The hover display, he feels, is a signal between adult birds attending nests, and it could have a variety of purposes such as speeding up feeding rates, facilitating communal food gathering, or synchronizing visits by the nest helpers. Dr Greig-Smith tends to the view that hovering most likely promotes communal foraging by the adults: communication as an aid to food acquisition. This is something that animals do frequently, and is a theme we shall return to in Chapter Seven.

Scents and sociability

In 1908 Helen Keller wrote that, in spite of her blindness, she could still identify people by what she called their 'person-odour'. Having lost the channel of vision, she had compensated to some extent by sharpening her sense of smell, a capacity that for most of us has all but disappeared in the course of human evolutionary history. This makes us quite rare among mammals. Of the 4000 or so mammalian species, only the cetaceans (whales and their relatives) appear to lack the physical apparatus for secreting scents for communication purposes. In the opinion of two authorities on the so-called 'social odours' of mammals, Dr David Macdonald and Dr Richard Brown, 'most mammals are surrounded by a penumbra of odours which are doubtless as much part of their social personas as are bared fangs or wagging tails.' The point is well made because in addition to being an instrument of social cohesion, an odour can also serve to deter and repel.

Mammals usually possess special skin glands which can generate these social odours for purposes of communication. But these substances can emanate from other areas as well. Urine, faeces, saliva, ear-wax and the secretions from the vagina have all been identified as sources. The information content carried by these chemicals can be so elaborate that they can truly be said to form a detailed sign-language: researchers indeed talk about the study of mammalian 'semiochemistry'.

There is a vast inventory of animal behaviour regulated by these bodily social secretions and it is constantly being updated. One function is trail marking, leaving traces of urine or faeces in places where these will attract the attentions of others. Researchers have discovered a wide range of such practices, depending on the species involved and indeed the 'status' of the creature concerned. Female bush dogs urinate high up on tree trunks from a handstand position, while foxes, wolves and other canid species leave their traces on prominent landmarks. The wolf will normally choose to defecate and urinate along much-used trails and paths; but a low-status, lone wolf, a bit of a social outsider, will quite deliberately leave its mark off the beaten track. Some animals will go to great lengths to manufacture a suitable conspicuous trail-leaving site. There is a species of antelope, for instance, the oribi, which neatly shears off high grass and rubs it against scent-carrying glands in front of the eye. The hyena marks its territorial borders by 'pasting', rubbing its anal gland along a stalk of grass that is pulled between the hind legs. A male elk similarly thrashes out a suitable site in the vegetation; and

(*Overleaf*) A million pairs of eyes. Lesser flamingos on the sulphur Lake Bogoria, Kenya. The bigger the flock, the safer the individual.

the Brazilian giant otter tramples over a spot by the river bank to leave its trail.

Particular animals leave scent markings in special patterns. The so-called 'territorial' species, such as the red fox or the Indian mongoose, deposit their markings throughout their ranges, ensuring total coverage. The coyote and the Eurasian badger will make sure to deposit more urine in those parts of their territory that might be the subject of dispute. Clearly in such cases the animal wants to reaffirm its ownership of a particular patch. Its smells denote 'This is mine', along with the associated warning, 'Keep out'. Territoriality is clearly all-important, though some researchers have suggested that certain trail markings could be for mating purposes, perhaps to declare one's presence to the opposite sex, and for signalling to stray animals that this is the way to rejoin the herd.

There is, in fact, some debate among biologists over the precise function of social odours. It has been suggested, for instance, that certain of these powerful smells may pass on not merely straightforward territorial information but even aspects of an individual animal's physiological and emotional state. They might indicate, too, such important features as age and sex, changes in social status from dominant to subordinate or vice versa, reproductive condition and the 'smell of fear'. Odours might repel predators or protect infants. According to David Henry, they may also serve a 'book-keeping' function. The fox or coyote spend less time exploring empty sites where food has formerly been stored by another fox or coyote when these places have been marked with urine. The tent caterpillar, too, leaves a chemical trail signifying that a food source has been visited. The odour, argues Henry, could be telling the incoming forager, 'Don't bother to waste any time here. There's no food left.' If so, what a rich language indeed emanates from that small patch of dried urine.

Status, hierarchy and dominance

Many animal societies are, like ours, hierarchical in character. Among animals, as among humans, there is ample evidence of rank, class, inequality and even a kind of snobbery. They, too, have to recognize and come to terms with their social niche. Yet this is not necessarily fixed for all time, and often they are able to take steps to change the social structure.

Just as we can easily recognize that a bishop outranks a humble priest because he wears more impressive garments, so one member of an animal species will know which is a dominant creature through its overt badge of status. This is particularly so among birds, where social standing seems to go hand in hand with distinctive plumage. The white-crowned sparrow who bears the brightest black, white and brown stripes on its head appears to be the dominant member of a flock. Similarly among great tits, breadth of breast stripes apparently indicates status, while for the Harris sparrow it is a matter of how much black feathering adorns the head and bib.

How and why does plumage seem so effective in conferring status? In the cases of the bishop and the parish priest, or the five-star general and the private soldier, there is a man-made code of practice regulating styles of dress which everyone recognizes. Can we assume that, among birds there are similar sets of rules? If so, on what are they based? These status-related plumage variations do not appear to confer any individual competitive advantage. It is possible that the badges are purely arbitrary, but this is not a very comfortable fact for biologists to acknowledge. They are accustomed

Orbital scent marking. A klipspringer in the Wankie National Park, Zimbabwe, rubs a shoot with a marking chemical secreted from an eye gland.

to seeing the characteristics of animals as having evolutionary or adaptive significance; better, then, to postulate that the plumage variations indicate superiority in age or size. In short, it is difficult to know whether these avian markings really do constitute a genuine status signal to others in the flock.

To put the matter to the test, Sievert Roher of Washington University carried out a series of ingenious, pioneering 'marking' experiments. Having captured both dominant and subordinate Harris sparrows – the higher-ranking birds having darker head, throat and breast feathers – Roher dyed the feathers of subordinates to a darker shade. At the same time he bleached the plumage of the dominants, thus superficially reversing their status. The next stage was to release these modified birds back into their flocks to see whether they assumed the false status of their doctored plumage. They did not. In fact, all the experimental birds were attacked by the rest of the flock. The pseudo-dominants failed to reach their expected standing, nor did the pseudo-subordinates sink to the bottom of the pile.

The rather puzzling implication seemed to be that plumage was *not* an indicator of status at all. What really seemed to matter in the bird flocks studied by Roher was an individual's fighting ability. If a pseudo-dominant,

Getting a head start. The head stripes of white-crowned sparrows vary in brightness from bird to bird; so does their social standing.

when challenged, failed to rise to the occasion, it was promptly relegated to its rightful subordinate rank. If a pseudo-subordinate, however, showed its true colours with a ferocious counter-attack, it enjoyed social superiority, despite its deceptive coloration. But things were not quite that straight-forward. Roher's experiments, cunning as they were, seemed to have been flawed in that the pseudos were put back into existing social groups where they were treated universally as strangers and attacked. According to Dr Tim Roper of the University of Sussex '. . . the dyed and bleached birds may have been victimised because they were unfamiliar, not because they were exposed as cheats.'

Other marking experiments, however, do seem to suggest that manipu-lating a bird's plumage can change its flock status. Gary Fugle, at the University of California, painted low-status, juvenile white-crowned sparrows to re-semble adult males and females. When they were housed with other birds of the same age and sex, Fugle found that the pseudo-adults dominated unpainted juveniles. The markings really did seem to signal social superiority. Experiments with great tits by two Norwegian researchers, Torbjorn Jarvi and Marten Bakken, from the University of Trondheim, appear to corroborate these results; width of breast stripe seems to have great status significance. The scientists used ingenious radio-controlled models of great tits painted with varying breast stripes to 'defend' a bird table from other tits. When the incoming birds approached, the models turned and displayed their stripes in an aggressive manner. If the defender's stripe was broader than that of the attacker, the latter backed off. Thus breast markings appear in this case to serve as a clear signal of relative position in a dominance hierarchy.

Symbolic displays

In human society, status symbols can take many forms. Ostentatious or official-looking dress or uniform serve as personal marks of standing and importance. So too do our possessions, especially our homes. Stroll along the tree-lined avenues of Hollywood's Beverly Hills district and the opulent mansions of the movie stars and producers scream out at you, 'I'm rich and famous'. Observe the dachshund-shaped 'stretch' Cadillac limousine as it glides through Manhattan. It hardly makes a sound but seems to shout to the tops of the skyscrapers that the owner is, to put it baldly, a bigshot. Remark-ably, it now begins to look as if some animals, too, like to advertise their status by elaborate displays of material wealth.

Some species of birds, for example, build nests that go far beyond the basic needs of providing warmth and protection for parent and offspring. Indeed, they practise quite elaborate decoration. Magpies will pilfer human trinkets to brighten up their nests. The bowerbirds of New Guinea and Australia go to extraordinary lengths to build ostentatious palaces, which are *not* nests, decked out with a fascinating range of coloured objects.

What purpose might those decorations serve? One may be camouflage; another, it has been suggested, may even be a form of artistic expression. However, researchers now believe that the complex artefacts of the bower-bird are really markers of the male's status. The male bird collects everything it can find – blue feathers, snail shells, blossoms, bits of dead cicadas and other insects, snake skins, human artefacts – and even uses a dust and saliva mixture to 'paint' the bower, all designed to provide the female with significant information on his standing so that she can choose her mate.

Studies of bowerbirds in the wild indicate that the males who mate most successfully are precisely those who show the greatest diversity and richness of decoration on their bowers. What is more, a male will go out of its way to sabotage a rival's handiwork, stealing pieces of ornamentation from its structure or even attempting to demolish it altogether. The females, for their part, respond to the enticement. Female bowerbirds tend to play the field, visiting, on average, the bowers of three different prospective partners before finally settling on a mate, namely the one with the most inviting construction. So nature has contrived to give the bowerbird a technique for extending its physical attributes to enhance his appeal to a female. The relatively dowdy male bowerbird compensates for its uninteresting plumage in a manner that is unnecessary for the related bird of paradise. The female bowerbird falls in with the scheme of things, being impressed by such extravagant displays or ornamentation. Thus shows of status become an important social mechanism for capturing and maintaining sexual interest.

Knowing one's place

It is wrong to regard animal societies as ideal, democratic structures in which each member of the population has an equal say in the running of its utopia. Nothing could be further from the reality. Animals do not merely claim supremacy based on the external signs of status or the possession of a stronger, fitter body than the rest of the bunch, but also exhibit something much more subtle, approximating to the rigid class and caste systems in human societies. There is even a kind of between-species racialism. Take the ant species *Harpagoxenus americanus*. A colony consists of one queen, usually with about ten workers of various rankings, which the queen evidently recognizes and maintains. The workers, in turn, have at their command a team of several hundred slaves pressed into service from another species, the *Leptothorax* ant. In their studies of the slave-making worker ants of Massachusetts, Nigel Franks and Edward Scovell have discovered how this complex system appears to be maintained. The queen tends to demand food from the more dominant individuals in her work force, rarely soliciting nourishment from the lower ranks. In this way, suggest Franks and Scovell, she ensures that she drains off the resources of those who might be potential rivals.

The recruitment of slave-ants is a highly dangerous activity because an individual slave-making worker may well be attacked by any *Leptothorax* it discovers; but the researchers found 'an uneven division of labour and risk-taking'. The 'fall guys' tend to be subordinate workers, i.e. those least likely to conceive and therefore with least to lose by behaving altruistically. Another interpretation is that some of the risk-takers may, in fact, benefit from their encounters with *Leptothorax* by not returning home but remaining in the raided nests with the brood they have captured. Here they have the chance of developing a new labour force and themselves producing many offspring. 'For this reason,' conclude the researchers, 'a slave raid that produces a new nest may function more as a strategic mutiny than as an altruistic act that serves the queen.'

In social creatures such as ants, wasps and termites, there is evidence that the channel of communication enabling these sophisticated interactions to be maintained is often chemical in nature. Ants belonging to different castes in the hierarchy, for instance, emit distinctive chemicals. In a colony of Pharaoh's ants, according to the chemical ecologists J. P. Edwards and J. Chambers, the queen produces a substance in its exocrine glands called neocembrene, which acts as a 'queen-specific pheromone'. The chemical is not found either in worker ants or young, virgin queens, which suggested that its role might somehow be connected with the sexual development of unfertilized queens. Similar substances are known to be emitted by the queen honeybee in order to inhibit the rearing of new queens – a kind of mass contraception campaign on the part of the queen to maintain her standing in the hive. But Edwards and Chambers now tend to reject this explanation in favour of another which casts the pheromone as a queen-recognition substance enabling workers to identify reproductively active queens from other female colony members, thus ensuring the queen of the favours and attentions of her subjects.

Social stresses and strains

Although living together obviously has its advantages, for animals, as for ourselves, there are also negative aspects of social life. Some primate societies, for instance, have their fair share of competitiveness, jealousies and sexual wrangling. These may operate in such a way as to threaten, or even on occasions break down, an established social hierarchy. A case in point is the savannah-dwelling baboon. The complex baboon societies, based as they are on the familiar principle of a dominance hierarchy, are constantly being modified by struggles for group supremacy. Two subordinate males, for example, will jointly gang up on the dominant male of the troop in order to drive him away from a receptive female. One of the subordinates thereby gets a chance to mate. On another occasion this kind of cooperation may result in the second subordinate gaining access to the female, the two revolutionaries taking it in turns to benefit from their overthrow of the *de facto* leader. These constant attempts to undermine and assert dominance are mediated by vivid vocal and body language. Males have a range of complex signals which they transmit by raising and lowering their expressive eyebrows, to reveal or obscure a conspicuous light-coloured area around the eyes. They will also display extravagantly coloured genitals in an unequivocal assertion of dominant intent, accompanied by a varied assortment of warning calls. Female baboons, too, communicate their interest in the established or newly dominant male by emitting receptivity odours or, again, by displaying to the male a rear-end which has become, in response to her physiological state of fertility, brightly coloured. It is a clear message: 'I'm ready'.

Varieties of primate social signals

The social systems of the primates in general, not merely baboons, show the importance of communication in establishing, regulating and maintaining all kinds of relationships among individuals and groups. The Oxford ecologist J. S. Kingdon has investigated the role of visual signals and face patterns in the social life of the African forest monkeys, the guenons of the genus *Cercopithecus*, and has studied at least eight species in considerable detail. The guenons are particularly striking in that their facial patterns sometimes rival the plumage of birds in brilliance and colouring and complexity of design. Like baboons, too, the tree-living guenons also have a wide repertoire of facial expressions, as well as body postures, which they coordinate for various purposes in their social life. In fact, the guenons illustrate a common feature of animal communication systems, the combination of what one might call 'active' and 'passive' modes of expression. Passive modes are those conveyed by such features as body coloration, size, shape and markings,

A stately pleasure dome. The male bower bird puts the finishing decorative touches to a newly built bower designed to attract a mate.

while active modes comprise the calls, postures and facial expressions adopted by an animal in particular contexts.

Dr Kingdon catalogues a fascinating array of active-cum-passive modes of expression and how these relate to the social behaviour of the guenons. The rare *Cercopithecus hamlyni* species, living in dense montane and forest habitats of eastern Zaire, is relatively inconspicuous, with a grizzled grey, green and black coat and a fairly unremarkable facial marking. By guenon standards it is slow-moving, quiet and fairly shy, aggregating in single-male groups of ten or less. Its dominant visual feature is the bright blue scrotal area of its genitals. Living as it does in dense forest surroundings, *C. hamlyni* usually communicates by means of deep booming calls or hoots rather than by visual signals; its thin vertical face stripe has very limited potential for the latter purpose. Here, then, is a guenon species that generally tends to merge into its surroundings, thanks to its body coloration, using resonant calls and displaying its genitals when occasion demands. By contrast, Dr Kingdon cites *Cercopithecus diana* which is among the most brightly coloured and active of all guenons, living in the more exposed upper forest canopies west of Dahomey. Its face is a jet-black mask set like a bull's eye within a broad white bib and beard. The limbs are also prominently marked in sharp linear contrast and colours, so that the different postures adopted by the animal are instantly conspicuous through the changing geometric configuration of its markings. It literally speaks with its body, in no uncertain terms.

Whereas *C. hamlyni* is constantly threatened by ground-living predators

Mixed feelings. This male hamadryas baboon clearly intends to intimidate with an aggressive, teeth-baring threat display. At the same time, it is turning its back and displaying its genitals in a show of circumspect defiance.

It pays to advertise: the male black-faced vervet monkey, like the guenon, communicates non-verbally by means of its brightly coloured genitals.

such as the leopard and the golden cat, and thus benefits from having a dull, cryptic body that does not advertise its presence, *C. diana*, in the tops of trees, has little to lose by being brightly coloured. Indeed, the latter can use its markings positively as longer distance communication signals while the drabber *C. hamlyni* relies more on loud calls to signal its presence to females or to maintain social cohesion of its troop.

Group to group communication

In any animal society, as in our own, it is inevitable that one group will, sooner or later, be forced to communicate with another. Such contacts can be either hostile or friendly, and more often than not it is the former. Animals tend to encroach on other groups in order to secure their resources, in the form of food or sexual partners. Although individual groups may function successfully as coordinated societies, when two groups come together there is often plunder and bloodshed in the air.

Dorothy Cheney, who has examined group interactions in many species of monkeys and apes, finds, however, that the picture is not one of unrelieved, out-and-out hostility. Much depends on the social behaviour of the particular primate. Thus in species characterized by females who are dispersed throughout a territory, the latter rarely behave aggressively towards other females. It is only when they live in monogamous family groups that they tend to be hostile towards females from outside the group. Males, however, especially dominants, are almost invariably hostile to outsiders, seeing them as potential rivals for their mates.

By contrast, the gibbons of South-east Asia – small apes inhabiting the rain forests of countries such as Indonesia – do their best to avoid inter-group clashes altogether with a distinctive form of vocal signalling. They sing. Gibbons have a unique social system among hominoid primates. Monogamous, mated pairs of adults defend an exclusive territory, occupied just by themselves and their handful of offspring. Males and females frequently duet with each other in a coordinated series of 'wa' and 'hoo' calls, modulated in patterns which have been carefully established and analyzed by the American primatalogist John Mitani, of the University of California. Dr Mitani found that these marital love duets can be heard just under half a mile away, so that 'one can assume that duets are reliably heard by neighbours holding ranges adjacent to singers'. Associating this idea with the times, circumstances, locations and certain other features of the songs, Mitani inclines to the view that 'dueting plays a role in intergroup spacing'. The patterns of the songs, in his opinion, vocally advertise and reinforce the gibbons' presence on their range, a view supported experimentally by his discovery that these apes increased the duration of their song bouts when apparently threatened by intrusion.

Understanding the social relationships of monkeys and apes may have important medical consequences. The marmoset, for example, is a creature much sought by biomedical researchers as a model system on which to carry out laboratory experimentation. Setting aside for the moment the much-debated question of ethical and moral considerations, it seems clear that the marmoset is for the time being likely to continue to be in demand, though in recent years there have been increasing restrictions on the number of animals available for research purposes. Thus captive breeding might well be the only means of ensuring a continued supply. However, animals bred in captivity do not always thrive as they do in the wild; and for this reason Gisela Epple, from the Monell Chemical Senses Center at the University of Pennsylvania, has been investigating the social behaviour of marmosets to see how this might be exploited to make for more successful captive breeding.

Some marmosets raised in captivity become aggressive and tend, according to Dr Epple, to be more prone to abortions, as well as spiteful towards their own family group. One sensible step, therefore, seems to be to house captive animals in cages that provide a certain amount of isolation from neighbouring groups, giving the animals no visual contact and therefore lowering their general level of excitement. In this way, too, it might be possible to decrease the level of infanticide observed in these species.

Rules and regulations

All effective societies must have their rules, laws, conventions and codes of conduct; sets of working principles that each member knows, understands and, for the most part, abides by. Wasps advertise these rules chemically.

The various members of the colony, with their allotted socio-economic role as males, workers or queens, possess a complicated system of scent markings that act as 'calling cards' to others. Sticky drops of member-specific chemicals, secreted by a gland in the wasp's abdomen, carry with them a social run-down on the creature that has deposited them. It is not unlike the process operating in ant communities should a member of another colony arrive suddenly in the nest. The host ants know immediately whether the newcomer is friend or foe. However, there is one curious difference. Whereas wasps secrete their own self-identifying pheromone, the acceptability chemical among ants appears to be distributed by the queen. In a series of ingenious experiments, Dr Bert Holldobler was able to establish that the queen endows her own daughters, or indeed any fostered workers, with the necessary chemical to prevent them being attacked. In fact, so powerful is this chemical mark of 'belonging' that it can even override the bonds of kinship. Fostered workers will attack their own sisters that have been reared in a different nest by a different queen, as if they were totally alien.

Bees, too, use chemical messengers in order to establish their social acceptability. In the sweat bee, which lives in quite small societies of only about six bees, one of the group is appointed 'immigration officer'. It sits at the entrance to the nest and only allows in those bees that secrete the necessary passport pheromone. The guard bee has remembered each of its fellow's odours individually, and can tell when an interloper is trying to force an entry.

A problem of thump and a conundrum of rumble

The more biologists find out about the social communication methods of animals, the more, apparently, there remains to discover. Take the case we saw earlier of the elephant with its low-frequency rumbling, as detected by Dr Katharine Payne. What social purpose might this serve? When these sounds are exchanged between males and females it seems reasonable to assume that they carry some mating function. The fact that the calls can travel over long distances would mean that a male might be able to detect a female

(*Above left*) Duetting siamangs in Sumatra, Indonesia. The adult male and female singers are accompanied by their child.

(*Above right*) A caring chimpanzee mother in the wild. Chimps in captivity though will often reject their offspring if the conditions are socially stressful.

Nature's megaphone. By expanding its vocal sac this common Central American frog produces an amplified croak.

as much as 5 miles away. This would accord with the wandering lifestyle of male elephants which move around in unstable all-male groups on the lookout for receptive females. The latter, incidentally, are only in oestrus for about a week to ten days a year, which makes well-timed, effective communication between the sexes imperative! However, female elephants also appear to exchange these rumbling calls among themselves. Why should they need to do so when they tend to aggregate in close, domestic groups? Why use an infrasonic call, apparently designed for long distance communication, when two individuals are close together? Only more insights into the social life of the elephant will resolve this question.

The male bullfrog represents another communicational puzzle. Recent research by Edwin Lewis and Peter Narins has established that the white-lipped frog not only communicates with a familiar series of croaks, whistles, clicks and buzzes. It also signals seismically by thumping the ground with its elasticated vocal sac. Why does this frog need a ground vibration generator when clearly it already possesses a wide vocal repertoire? One explanation is that the bullfrog uses this technique to estimate the location of its neighbours, and thus possibly to determine where his rivals are sitting. Another hypothesis is that seismic signalling may be a way of drawing attention to himself for the purposes of attracting a mate. Observations of frog societies have not thus far given a conclusive answer one way or the other. As with elephantine rumblings, the social significance of the thump of the male frog remains still to be deciphered.

In the next chapter we shall be looking further at the role of communication in social life, this time for the very specific (and important) purpose of courtship.

Chapter   Five

A Kaleidoscope
of Courtship

Courtship to marriage, as a very witty prologue to a very dull play.
William Congreve (1670–1729)

Anthropologists have long been aware of the enormous amount of time, energy, creativity and cunning expended by humans of all cultures in finding and attracting a suitable mate. The act of mating itself, the physical consummation of reciprocated feelings, is but a relatively brief final stage in what is often a long, elaborate series of interpersonal opening encounters that go by the general title of 'courtship'. Before two individuals are committed irrevocably to each other, they have revelled in such preliminary rituals as present-giving, displays of strength or affection, exchanges of letters, and innumerable other ploys designed to impress, flatter, cajole or sometimes rebuke. Study of animal behaviour reveals that we are not alone in deploying elaborate courtship strategies and methods. And, in all these pre-mating games, with animals as with us, communication plays a key role.

Before we look at this behaviour in more detail, we ought perhaps to ask ourselves simply why animals should go in for this kind of activity in the first place. After all, nature is for the most part thrifty. Natural organisms rarely do things that will consume precious energy without some ultimate advantage or evolutionary purpose to their efforts. Courtship seems to serve a number of important functions.

First, the complex rituals that we often observe male animals performing in front of their chosen female appear to convey a strong signal to her of his fitness as a sexual partner. The female is looking for a mate who is well-endowed physically, thereby capable both of passing on to her offspring genes that promote strength and health. Physical fitness may also be useful for protecting the female and any offspring, and for hunting for their food. What better way, then, to convey fitness than by a display of fine, glowing colours or a large, strong body? A second function of courtship is organizational. It ensures that both partners are in the right place, at the right time, for mating to occur. In addition, the act of wooing appears to stimulate the female, as well as producing a degree of synchrony in both animals' physiological and sexual mechanisms. Thus courtship serves as a preliminary regulator of coordinated physical union. It also helps to break down any barriers that might normally introduce distance between individuals, such as natural inclinations to be aggressive towards, or to flee from, a strange animal. And the specific rituals of courtship are a guard against cross-mating between species. Finally, courtship progressively seems to produce a sense of commitment between the partners-to-be, an increasingly strong bond that will help to keep them together as a pair, at least for as long as is necessary for successful mating.

Corals need no courtship. Like sponges, they leave fertilization to chance.

Absent friends

Not *all* animals, however, need to court in order to mate. Sponges, corals and hydra release eggs into the water where they may or may not be fertilized by any randomly deposited sperm that happens to be floating around. Male springtails – tiny, wingless insects that live in leaf litter – release sperm in little packages called 'spermatophores'. Should a female happen to brush against one of these, it will open, releasing the cells that can, again somewhat haphazardly, find their way to her genital opening.

There are also a very few creatures that have no need for courtship because they do not require another sexual partner to fertilize their eggs. These are the so-called 'self-fertilizing' species, such as the killfish that inhabits the coastal ponds of Florida and islands of the Gulf of Mexico. The habitat is very unpredictable because waters alternately flood in and dry out, often leaving the killfish stranded on its own. Thus it has evolved a method for doing without a partner in order to reproduce. Then there are those species such as the lizards living in the south-west of the USA, or the strange molly fish of the Amazon, that dispense with fertilization altogether, practising parthenogenisis or 'virgin birth'. Again, no courtship is necessary here. But in the overall picture of animal mating behaviour, these are just a few isolated exceptions.

Contexts for courtship

The 'singles bar' is surely one of our more effective pieces of social engineering. Here, you can be sure, there is one and only one purpose in the minds of the clientele: to meet a member of the opposite sex. The sole reason for its existence is to facilitate sexual encounters; and if clients are disappointed in repeatedly failing to find the man or woman of their dreams, that, as they say in all disclaimer notices, is no fault of the management. The concept of a well-defined, unequivocally identifiable meeting ground for would-be sexual partners is well established, and has many echoes elsewhere in the animal kingdom.

The albatross, a solitary, ocean-living bird for most of the year, forsakes its great, gliding flights during the breeding season when it gathers in large numbers on remote islands in order to mate. One member of the gannet family, Abbott's booby, chooses just one spot, namely Christmas Island in the Indian Ocean, for its annual bout of courtship. In both cases these birds have gone to extraordinary lengths simply to navigate their way back to the appointed meeting places.

Although time is relatively short, these species do not experience the frenetic pressure to win a mate that burdens the European common frog. The frog is an 'explosive breeder', meaning it often has a mere two days in which to fertilize or be fertilized, so that any courtship rituals have to be severely curtailed if the species is to continue to reproduce successfully. Thus in the spring, all frogs, male and female, converge in huge numbers on ponds and ditches where they form a writhing mass of rapidly mating creatures with a singleness of purpose that makes the orgies of Caligula's

Lifelong companions. When these two albatrosses of the Galapagos Islands mate, they will come back to the same spot every year to continue their courtship.

Toads, like frogs, are explosive breeders. A mass of males are attempting to mate with a single female.

Rome look positively sedate. There is simply not enough time for such niceties, for example, as males monopolizing females. Even so, these rapid-fire couplings do not appear altogether random. Males tend to mate with females roughly the same size, suggesting that bodily proportions are an important dominant visual cue in making one frog more attractive than another.

Many species of insect, fish and mammal utilize special confined areas given over exclusively to mating, where adult males assemble and wait to be visited by females solely for the purpose of copulation. The males compete hotly for these so-called 'leks'; and in a role reversal of their human

Areas of interest. A male prairie grouse on a 'lek' showing off his colourful plumage in order to attract a mate.

counterparts in dancehalls and discos, they are then appraised and 'chosen' by females. On what grounds to females make their choice? Careful attempts to determine the decisive factors have so far, according to Jack Bradbury and Robert Gibson, proved inconclusive. Indeed, they contend that 'we are only beginning to understand which cues are used by females to choose mates on leks.' The widely accepted notion that females simply choose the central or dominant male on a lek is not, in their opinion, tenable in the face of the facts. Even when females are unanimous in their selection of partner, it may be that some are copying the choice of others, without themselves attempting to discriminate between males. Alternatively, other factors altogether may be operating to influence choice. Among the frog species *Physalaemus postulosus*, for example, although body size and mating success seem to be correlated, a better guarantee would appear to be the amount of time spent by the male frog in calling. When two independent researchers studied the distinctive strut of the male sage grouse during lekking, they came to precisely opposite conclusions as to whether successful males strutted at higher rates than unsuccessful birds. Then there is the copycat theory. Research on the hammer-headed bat shows that after copulation females emit a loud squeal, which, it has been suggested, acts as a signal to other females to choose the same male for a mate. Age, body size, vigour or any other conventional masculine 'qualifications' may have nothing to do with a particular male being chosen, or if they do, only indirectly.

Street-corner strategies

Another way for the sexes to arrange an initial encounter is for one of them to hang around those places most likely to be visited by the other. For an animal, that usually means remaining close to a source of food. The males of nectar- and pollen-eating insects, such as bees and wasps, position themselves near flowers, hovering around in the hope and expectation that, eventually, a female will happen along. The male dungfly, having detected a freshly deposited cowpat, hovers downwind in order to intercept any virgin females attracted to the dung as a suitable breeding site. Needless to say, more than one male will often get the same idea and there is likely to be some street-corner scuffling among competitors for the favoured meeting place.

There can be other disadvantages, too, for certain males attempting to use food sources as a courting ground. The fly orchid, in order to ensure that it wastes as little as possible of its pollen, advertises its presence to the male of a certain species of wasp, *Argogorytes mystaceus*, by releasing quantities of the wasp's female pheromone. The male, detecting this attractant chemical, flies to the orchid and attempts to mate with the lip of the flower, a small, furry growth that roughly mimics the female's body shape. The male is further bamboozled by other features of the flower such as its nectaries, which resemble the female wasp's eyes. The outcome, anyway, of the deceived male's thrusting is that sticky pollen sacs become attached to his abdomen, there to be transported to other flowers. So much, then, for food sources as a playground for the two sexes!

It pays to advertise

Many initial contacts between animals are made, not on defined meeting grounds, but at a distance, using a variety of signals involving sight, sound or smell. Again there are potential dangers. The male has to perform a kind of cost-benefit analysis when it advertises its presence to a female because these same signals may well be intercepted by a predator. The frog-eating bat, for example, specializes in picking off its prey once the latter has made itself obvious through mating calls. Likewise, the snapping turtle of North America makes a good living by pouncing on the highly vocal bullfrog. Thus certain mating species will actually switch communication channels between, say, sight and sound in an attempt to outwit a predator.

Visual courtship displays for catching the eye of (usually) a female can assume colourful, even dramatic forms. How could a dull, brown peahen fail to be impressed by the magnificent, shimmering plumage of the peacock? The female of the great bustard, too, is treated to a riveting courtship display by the male who, remaining silent all the while, effects an astonishing self-transformation. Normally his plumage is brown, grey and black but by throwing the tail forward and the wings back, he reveals a huge mass of billowing white feathers, turning himself into a conspicuous fluffy ball that will be visible to the female far across the open plains where they live.

The cabbage white butterfly similarly relies on catching sight of a flash of white to find its mate, but has evolved a strategy for protecting itself against predators in the process. The cabbage white feeds on plants containing mustard oil, which it stores in some quantity within its body. The substance is a built-in deterrent because it tastes horrible to birds, which therefore tend to leave the butterfly to its own devices.

Courtship signs that depend on the sense of sight have their drawbacks. Vision is of limited value in the water or at night, while the fact that light cannot travel around corners restricts its usefulness in areas of relatively dense vegetation or undulating, rocky terrain. The firefly, like the glow-worm, gets round the problem of attracting a mate in the dark by using its special luminescent organs. With the glow-worm it is the female that does the displaying, turning her abdomen skyward so that searching males catch sight of the biological beacon of light. Among fireflies, however, it is the male that displays, using his luminous signals like a kind of flying Morse code with short-long pulses. These messages are evidently very distinctive to different species. Indeed, they need to be because many species of firefly share the same habitats and choose to do their courtship on precisely the same nights.

The signalling of the male firefly is answered by flashes from the female, and thereby hangs a potential threat for certain species. Female fireflies of the genus *Photuris* prey on males of the genus *Photinus*. They do so by mimicking the flashing lights from *Photinus* females, thereby attracting a male which flies down to develop this incipient relationship only to find himself the supper, not the suitor, of the waiting female. It is a telling example of natural deception. There are many more, as we shall see in Chapter Seven.

Flash of the *femme fatale*. Light-emitting female glow-worms advertise their presence to passing males.

Sounds interesting

Sounds are another effective way in which animals communicate during courtship. Not only can calls carry much important and subtle information, they also obviate some of the difficulties of visual signalling, enabling a male, for example, to advertise his wares without making himself visually conspicuous to a predator.

We have seen that the voice is not essential for sound communication. Other parts of the body can also be used effectively in courtship. The grasshopper rubs its hindlegs against its wings to produce complicated song structures, while crickets and bush crickets rub their two wings together to emit sounds of varying durations. Perhaps the most penetrating insect call of all is that of the cicada. The male's sound-production mechanism consists of two hard plates called 'tymbals' on either side of its thorax. By rapidly flexing strong muscles, the insect manages to buckle and unbuckle these plates to produce its characteristic ticking sound. What is more, the male cicada has a volume control over his songs – a special covering that acts as a damper when it is lowered. This, combined with a prodigiously fast output of ticks that can reach up to 1000 per second, gives the cicada an instrumental voice of some versatility for charming a prospective mate.

Insect calls, like visual courtship displays, can also be intercepted by a predator. The cricket, whose song is almost exclusively used for courtship and mating purposes, has evolved two strategies for meeting this contingency. It has, in addition, a back-up courting dance which it can perform without any sound accompaniment. Alternatively, it uses a cunning avoidance mechanism in the form of a signal 'jamming' technique. The bat is one of the cricket's chief enemies, and bats use a form of sonar echo-location to help them detect prey. So the cricket sings in unison with other crickets in such a way as to jam the sonic frequencies used by the prowling bat.

One species of cricket, the mole cricket, displays acoustic skills of an even more sophisticated nature by digging burrows that act as megaphones, amplifying the sounds they produce to catch the attentions of females. The bullfrog, too, uses amplification from a built-in sound box in the form of a huge, balloon-shaped throat pouch. The mating signals of frogs have received a lot of attention from researchers in recent years, including Bob Capranica and Peter Narins, who have made a special study of one tree-dwelling species from Puerto Rico called *Eleutherodactylus coqui*. The 'coqui' in its name refers to the fact that the male has a two-note call – a 'co' sound at a fixed frequency and a 'qui' note at a higher frequency. Sitting in the rain forests

of Central America, the tree frog uses this call at night to attract females. But Narins and Capranica have found that it also deploys the song to ward off other males. Could one of the co-qui notes, they wondered, be aimed at females, the other at males? Sure enough, after some playback experiments on frogs in the wild, they established that this is indeed the case. The 'qui' component is the mating part of the call, intended for females whose ears are selectively tuned to precisely the frequency of that note, while 'co' is a signal to would-be intruders to keep off the patch. Thus the tree frog, in one short song, is saying 'come hither' and 'scram!' simultaneously.

The calls of birds are often intended to attract the opposite sex. Indeed, according to Dr Clive Catchpole, the prime function of birdsong is probably courtship: it is the acoustic equivalent of, say, flamboyant plumage. Dr Catchpole has studied the song of various species of European warblers such as the reed, marsh and sedge warbler common in the British Isles. The male birds find a suitable singing site, give out their elaborate song and wait for females to take up their offers. Once a female has responded to the appeal and formed a pair, the male stops singing – a firm indication, argues Dr Catchpole, that the song has served its main function. Warblers' songs are extremely complex, consisting of dozens of individual acoustic elements arranged and rearranged endlessly to form novel combinations that are apparently never repeated. Dr Catchpole's experiments showed that this very elaboration is important in the bird's sexual success. The more of a virtuoso the male proves to be, the sooner he attracts a female.

'Qui' means courtship in the 2-note calling language of the Puerto Rican tree frog.

Wings of song. The male tree cricket rasping its wings together to produce its mating call.

75

Body language

We humans tend to think of ourselves communicating with one another solely in the symbolic medium of spoken or written language. But we are mistaken. We also speak volumes through our body actions because, for all our civilization, we retain much of our animal heritage. We are, in the words of Dr Desmond Morris, '. . . a gesticulating, posturing, moving, expressive primate'. Follow the example of the social psychologist and watch people interacting in familiar situations, especially males and females together. Even without knowing what they are saying, you can learn an enormous amount about their attitudes and intentions because these are revealed, betrayed even, by what is unspoken. The turn and tilt of the body, facial expression, general physical demeanour, all indicate interest or boredom, affection or contempt, and a whole range of more subtle shades in between.

One of the most unequivocal forms of body language is the dance. Watch couples on a dance floor and you can gauge the progress and comparative success of the courtship rituals that are taking place. Dancing as a means of attracting a mate has a long history, of course, in both human and animal societies. The sage grouse in his lek is an arch-exponent, strutting in eye-catching fashion while showing off his plumage and accompanying himself with a loud booming call. Unlike the dance-hall ritual, however, it is the female grouse who strolls along to inspect what is on offer. Similarly, the male mayfly puts on a flamboyant show of formation dancing in the company of a swarm of other males, in order to attract females. He performs with an aerobatic flourish, flying upwards then gently parachuting down again, for hours on end, until a female comes on the scene. Thereafter things deteriorate into a wild brawl, with groups of males hanging on to one female until one manages to mate with her. Saturday Night Fever indeed!

There has been no more keen observer of the courtship body language of animals, especially of various duck species, than that founding father of modern ethology, Konrad Lorenz. In one classic film, Lorenz shows in great detail the whole characteristic courting language of the mallard, beginning with the spring moult and the male bird in fine nuptial plumage.

First comes an extended attraction call, a signal to females as well as other drakes that the individual is here and ready to do business. Then the drake adopts a preliminary stance, unmistakably to compel attention, head drawn back between the shoulders, head plumage ruffled, and body floating high in the water. Meanwhile the females have begun to form a circle of attentive spectators. Courtship proper starts with a lateral shake of the bill, which gets more and more urgent, culminating in the so-called 'grunt-whistle' whereby the bird bends over so that his bill touches the water and at that moment gives it a lateral jerk which ejects a series of water droplets. Next moment the drake's breast is sharply pulled out of the water, head still down, so that the neck is bizarrely curved. This arching induces tension in the bird's windpipe and a piercing whistle emerges. The body then reverts to its normal position, whereupon a low-pitched grunt is heard: hence grunt-whistle.

The male mallard also has a further sequence of optional moves for communicating with, and perhaps enticing, a partner. A 'down-up' movement draws a column of water upwards, and a 'head-up-tail-up' manoeuvre, raising head and tail simultaneously to form a 'U'-shaped configuration of the body exposes the otherwise hidden, spectacular tail feathers. The female now joins in all this body talk and the pair pursue the courtship pattern with such activities as 'nod-swimming', 'bridling', 'mock-preening' and 'inciting'; this last action is performed by the female, after a certain amount of foreplay, called 'pumping', in which the head is moved vertically up and down and the bill held out horizontally, to stimulate the male to the point of copulation. Although we should not stretch the comparisons too far, there are parallels here with human courtship behaviour. 'The function of this movement,' writes Lorenz of the mallard, 'is without doubt mutual stimulation of the mates and the synchronization of their reactions.' Those might well be the words of the author of a book on human sexuality.

Attractive odours

As in many other areas of animal communication, smell plays an important role in conveying and receiving courtship messages. To us, with our barely existent sense of smell, this may seem a relatively inferior way of getting across important information, but for some species olfactory signals are as sharply informative as any extravagant visual display or courtship song.

Among insects, these courtship pheromones are highly developed. In order to advertise her presence to males, the female silk moth disperses tiny amounts of a substance called bombykol into the atmosphere. The male detects this through special receptor cells in its antennae, so sensitive that only one molecule of bombykol is sufficient to fire off a reaction. Likewise the male vapourer moth can pick up minute traces of a female attractant chemical as much as 5 miles (8 km) away from the point of emission.

Yet olfactory messages, too, may be intercepted by predators. The female southern pine bark beetle, in using a chemical attractant to signal to males of the species, will make her presence known to the clerid beetle, thus trading off reproductive success against potential self-sacrifice.

Scents for attracting the opposite sex can be effective not only in the atmosphere but in water. The use of such chemicals by female Mississippi catfish is exploited by local fishermen who bait traps with live females secreting the pheromone, thus luring the males, siren-like, to their doom.

On land, chemical mating calls are commonplace. Female adders leave behind scent trails to be sampled, in a combination of tasting and smelling, by the sensitive sense organs in the male's tongue. The common house mouse, like certain other mammal species, but especially other rodents, has a kind of auxiliary nose, the 'vomero-nasal organ', through which it sniffs and inhales alien scents. It is a natural apparatus of enormous importance in the communication of courting signals.

The use of chemical signals by rodents has been investigated by Richard Doty of the Monell Chemical Senses Center at the University of Pennsylvania, one of the world's leading laboratories for this form of animal communication. Dr Doty finds that research by other workers in this field has tended to present a somewhat lopsided picture. Male rodents are known to employ odours in much the same way as males of other species use visual or acoustic courting displays. Males use large specialized glands for manufacturing and secreting mating odours that indicate to likely partners their fitness as mates. However, says Doty, this does not mean that females are simply the passive recipients of male attentions. There is evidence that 'equal opportunity' research will show that 'the female of many rodent forms plays a more important role in the initiation and maintenance of courtship and copulatory activities than has been generally believed'.

In what he calls 'a cry for the liberation of the female rodent', Richard Doty argues that the determining factor in choosing an appropriate mating

On the scent of a partner. The golden marmoset of Brazil communicates chemically, leaving odours to attract the opposite sex.

partner may be the female's ability to discriminate between male odours. She has to possess the right sensory apparatus to make her choice, just as the male must have the right equipment to give her the opportunity of so doing. In other words, the scent-mediated courting behaviour of rodents shows genuine reciprocity, with females playing a more active role in courting than has hitherto been admitted.

Humans, of course, have long been obsessed with attractant odours. There is a colossal world-wide perfume, cologne and aftershave industry which assiduously exploits our perennial desire to 'smell nice' and, by implication, 'smell attractive'. Compared to other primates, however, our sense of smell is woefully inadequate. Among marmoset monkeys, for instance, one animal is able to determine from odour alone the traces left by a member of the opposite sex. Meanwhile the monkey that has left his marking chemical can wander elsewhere depositing similar traces, thereby maximizing his chances of securing a partner. In their study of saddle-back tamarins, a member of the marmoset monkey family dwelling in the forests of upper Amazonia, a team of researchers lead by Gisela Epple looked in detail at this form of communication, in order to determine for how long these courtship odours remain effective. They found that scents left by male tamarins, presenting as they do a 'complex and specific stimulus' that elicits a good deal of sniffing and marking of the area by the female, continued to attract females strongly for at least 24 hours. Then the activity declined, according to environmental conditions, so that after three to four days the scent marks were no longer of interest to other animals. It also emerged from this study that a female could identify the gender of the scent-marker up to two days after the odour was deposited, but not longer; yet cues as to the identity of the marker's species continued to be detectable for the full three-to-four-day period. The female can therefore, over a period of a few days, derive from the chemical substances secreted by the male tamarin a wide range of information that is of crucial importance in influencing her to mate: the species of the individual donor, its sex, gonadal state and possibly rank within its particular dominance hierarchy – all of which adds up to the monkey's equivalent of a computer-dating profile.

Given the potency of the naturally occurring chemicals that make up these attractants, it is hardly surprising that we have borrowed some of them for exploitation in our own courtship rituals. Musk, civitone and castor, the chemical compounds that act as mating cues respectively for the deer, the civet cat and the beaver are widely employed as a base in the cosmetics and

Small-toothed palm civet cat, a source of the attractant chemical civitone used in the perfume industry.

perfumery world. How ironic it is that we should do so. We liberally apply the scents of animals to our necks or armpits while doing our level best to suppress our own, natural smells with deodorants and anti-perspirants. If, in the bodily secretions of other species, there are tiny amounts of powerful attractant chemicals designed by evolution to trigger off the responses of the opposite sex, why not in our species as well? Perhaps we, too, secrete courtship pheromones. It is an intriguing notion.

We may well possess especially sensitive smell receptors in our brain that are attuned to minute quantities of stimulant chemicals, including attractant perfumes. What is more, so strong may be the pull exercised by these receptors that we might literally be led by the nose if some politician or military leader chose to exploit them for behaviour control purposes. Imagine our moods, our social behaviour or our sexual lives being regulated by smells. The urine odours of an unfamiliar male mouse, when detected by a recently inseminated female of the species, have the effect of blocking the pregnancy. Conversely, once a female pig has been sprayed with the male pig pheromone, the sow immediately adopts the characteristic, crouched mating posture, even though there is no boar in the vicinity. If, among animals, pheromones can dictate fertility or conception, perhaps our mating behaviour, too, might be regulated, with or without our consent, by the hidden persuaders that enter through our nostrils.

Telephone-call courtship

The more biologists discover about animal behaviour, the less original do our man-made technologies appear to be. At the famous Scripps Institute of Oceanography in California, Mary Hagedorn and Walter Heiligenberg, studying the courtship behaviour of *Eigenmannia* fish species discovered that individuals signal to each other using a method that is the natural equivalent of the telegraph. After observing more than 600 hours of fish courting and mating activity, the researchers established that the male, as he woos a female, indicates his presence by a series of electrical pulses, discharged from a special electric organ. The initial mating call of the male, signifying 'I'm here. I'm strong. I'm ready', takes the form of rapidly pulsed 'chirps'. If the female is interested, she responds with her own electrical call, slowly increasing her discharge rate in what is termed a 'long rise', which is maintained for about ten seconds, then drops back to the resting level. By playing back male chirps to females, Hagedorn and Heiligenberg were able to induce them to spawn, even with no male fish in the tank. Dominant males also have a characteristic low-frequency courtship signal. Again, when this was played back to females, the latter immediately went into their long-rise reaction. This indication of the extreme importance of electrical language among fish is supported by the work of a British scientist Dr Max Westby, who has also identified among *Eigenmannia* threat and submission signals, communicated from the electric organ.

Who chooses whom, and why?

Throughout this chapter we have been observing courtship behaviour as a true two-way communication exercise, with males displaying their interest, qualifications and intentions while females, for the most part, make their assessments and come to a decision. Although few if any biologists today would dispute the female's capacity for choice, this is not always obvious, nor has it always been recognized. Charles Darwin, originator of the theory

An imperial mating display from the magnificent male emperor bird of paradise, seen here on the Huon Peninsula of Papua New Guinea. The more extravagant the plumage, the better his chances of success.

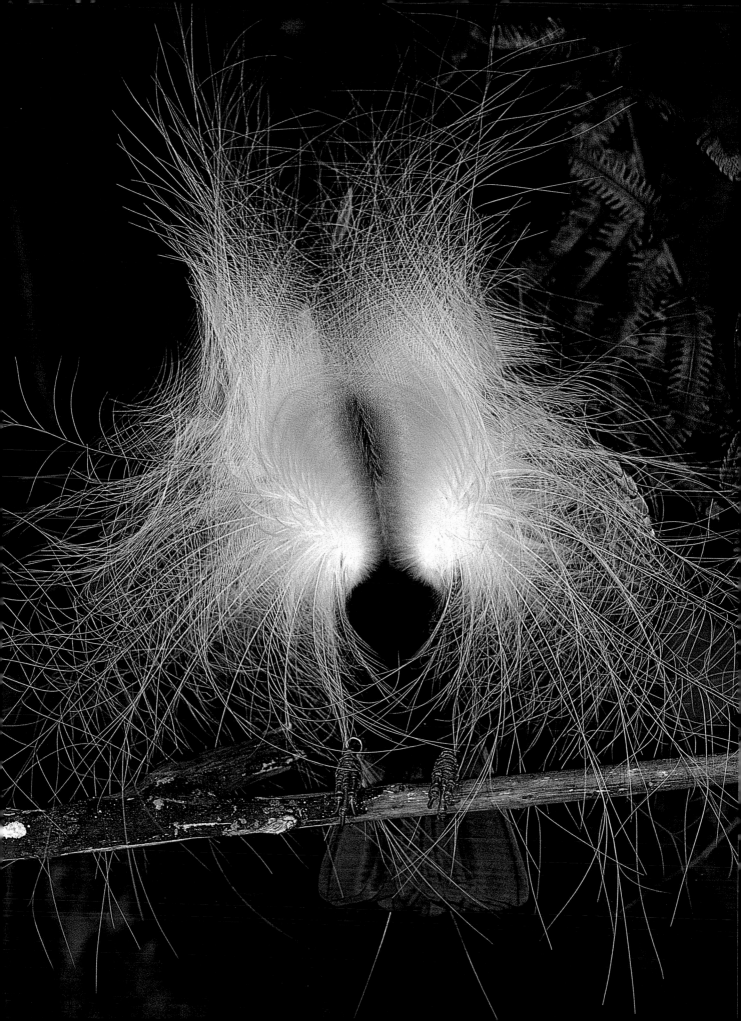

of evolution based on natural selection, contended that the ornate plumage of hummingbirds, bowerbirds, birds-of-paradise and the like, had two evolutionary functions: in male-to-male confrontations and in the attraction of females. The co-discoverer of natural selection, Alfred Wallace, disputed this. He did not agree that female choice had any importance in mate selection, doubting whether females of non-human species had the mental apparatus to distinguish between males competing for her favours.

Subsequently, however, evidence has accumulated that this is probably not the case. We saw in Chapter Four the lengths to which male bowerbirds will go to impress females. Similarly, the male scorpion fly has to offer a female a substantial amount of nuptial food before she will consent to mate. A study of the male guppy fish by Robert Bischoff and his colleagues at Princeton University demonstrated, under laboratory conditions (where there could be no ambiguity in the operation of the mate selection mechanism), that female guppies prefer males with a large tail, as well as with higher display rates. 'This appears,' say the researchers, 'to be a case of female-choice sexual selection.'

In fact, as Richard Doty observed in rodents, females are increasingly being shown to take a more active role in the courtship process than was suspected. Research reveals, in fact, that in a small number of species, as appears to be happening in a few corners of some human societies, 'role reversal' takes place in the preliminaries to copulation. Certain females behave like conventional males, with dominant courtship behaviour or with striking physical characteristics such as large size, display coloration and a measure of aggressiveness in competing for males. This has been observed in vertebrates such as birds and fish, and even in a few invertebrates including the fruit fly and some butterflies. Marea Hatziolos and Roy Caldwell, two zoologists at the University of California, Berkeley, added to this list when they studied the courtship of a crustacean, the stomatopod called *Pseudosquilla ciliata*. This is a solitary marine predator, living in coral reefs where it picks off small fish and smaller crustaceans with a single strike of its efficient claws. Its courtship displays have been well documented, and include a characteristic approach body language: a physical display; a rhythmic jerking beat of the pleopods; touching; and a rapid, head-on stylized pass called a 'cant'. Courtship is generally initiated by the female, whose eagerness is in striking contrast to the reluctance of the male. Of 57 encounters studied, the researchers found that females made the running on 43 occasions.

A likely partner found and a courtship completed, whichever of the pair takes the initiative, the next step is mating, and all that this entails.

Chapter Six

Family Matters

The manager of a particularly successful British soccer team was once accused of elevating his sport to the status of A Matter of Life and Death. 'Oh, no,' he is said to have replied, 'it's far more serious than that!' Observers of animal behaviour would probably substitute 'sex' for 'soccer', because mating games, if one can call them that, are the most earnest of all activities in the animal kingdom. Undoubtedly, the act of mating is the crucial reproductive event; the coming together of male and female (in those species that do reproduce sexually) is essential to the continued existence of the race. In nature's cup-tie competition, only a win is good enough to get the participants, here represented by their offspring, into the next round.

At this point our comparison between sport and sex begins to wear thin, because whereas a game of soccer is a uniform affair, with the standard eleven players, a whistle-toting referee, an allotted time span and a universal set of rules, animal mating, including systems of looking after the young, shows a vast range of practices from species to species. Nor is it especially apt, either, to think of mating as a 'game'. Consider, for example, the exploits of certain species of spider. As a tiny male spider approaches his relatively huge mate and begins to couple, the bulky female seizes him

Speed is essential for the male crab spider intent on mating. Unless he completes the act quickly the huge female devours him.

and starts to devour him in an act of copulatory cannibalism. She chews away the head, leaving the rest of the male's body sexually functional, so that his sperm can continue to pass into her body.

So predatory are female spiders that some males have had to develop diversionary strategies that enable them to complete the sexual act without falling victim to their partner's non-sexual appetites. There is, for instance, the male that offers the female a tasty morsel as a gift so that he can mate with her while she feeds. Some species actually package the food offering in an elaborate silk cocoon that takes the intended some time to unravel. Food diversions are also employed by males working in teams. While some bring nourishment to occupy the female's mouth, another male mounts, copulates and makes an unscathed getaway.

Alternatively, the male tarantula has a pair of curved appendages on its front legs which it deploys to great effect, holding open the female's jaws so that she cannot snap at him during their union. One type of crab spider even seems to practice a form of arachnid bondage. The male partially immobilizes the female with silk threads that strap her down; the fact that she can still wriggle about quite a bit suggests perhaps that, under this quasi-sadistic guise, there operates a degree of stimulation akin to that experienced by humans who take delight in bizarre sexual practices.

Acts of union

One of the striking aspects of the act of copulation among animals is that the time involved varies considerably. While the greater bushbaby will spend more than two hours, some gazelles manage to achieve their ends in a matter of a few seconds, and that while walking. Frequency, too, varies from species to species. Some copulate only once a year, while others such as the lion have been observed to mate at an average interval of twelve minutes. One male in a pride attained a Herculean score of 86 matings in a single day.

There is even more variety in the nature of the physical act itself. In some mammal species the male tries to ensure the female's complete cooperation by immobilizing her. The polecat, for instance, places his paws on the female's shoulder and bites her neck, inducing, for fifteen minutes, a condition of muscular paralysis. Many species separate after union, but some remain tied together in a post-copulatory lock. This has been observed in marsupials, rodents, dogs and primates, although no one is quite sure why it occurs. One suggestion is that it serves as a warning signal from the male to other males to reduce competition – a kind of 'do not disturb' notice.

Mating may take place face-to-face, face-to-back and back-to-back, with a number of interesting variants on these basic positions. It can occur on land or in the water; and it can be silent or noisy. The male rhesus monkey will chew and gnash its teeth while copulating, baring the teeth and squealing at the moment of ejaculation; meanwhile the female smacks her lips, stares round at her mate and also lets out squeals.

Although the male is usually the active partner, trying to keep the female relatively still in order to ensure the transfer of his sperm, this is not universal. When European newts mate, at no time does the male actually clasp the female. He simply stimulates her into receptivity by courtship displays with his tail. Having ensured the female's attention, he deposits a sperm-carrying spermatophore. He then blocks the female's path so that, effectively, she is obliged to bring her cloaca – the entry point for sperm – into contact with the spermatophore. In this way she picks up the male's seed.

Even when two animals are not actually joined in sexual union, therefore, they often need to exchange some information to regulate their mating. And when they do eventually come together, the inter-animal communication continues. Sounds or signs of mutual effort, encouragement, satisfaction and satiety are constantly being exchanged, as if to fine-tune a vital process at the crucial moments.

Cajolery, violence and other variants

Among animals the chief purpose of sex is procreation. But as with humans, not all acts of intercourse are necessarily designed to the specific immediate end of producing offspring. The male hummingbird of the island of Dominica in the Gulf of Mexico appears to buy sexual favours from females by allowing them to feed from the flowers of banana plants where he reigns dominant. Likewise, the hummingbird of Costa Rica offers gifts of nectar from the trees under his sway. This purchase of favours looks very like a form of prostitution, especially when it is seen to take place outside the breeding season when the sexual organs of the birds produce neither eggs nor sperm.

If bribery or cajolery are not appropriate, downright trickery can some-times enable the Don Juanesque male to get his way. Male Atlantic salmon will slip alongside females while they are mating with another and release their sperm at precisely the same moment as their rival. Or there are more aggressive strategies such as that of the parasitic thorny-headed worm that lives in the intestines of rats. The male has a special gland for secreting a kind of cement that plugs up the genital opening of females, thus preventing others from mating with her. But not content with this chastity belt for females, the worm goes one further and inserts the plug into the reproductive tract of other males, thus rendering them unable to continue taking advantage of the female anyway.

As well as prostitution, subterfuge and underhanded contraception, we also see behaviour that looks very much like rape. Male top minnows seem to force copulation with unwilling females, as do mallard ducks, the latter changing from monogamous, protective fathers to promiscuous gadabouts once the females have laid their clutches of eggs. It is quite common to see male mallards on a pond moving around in groups on the lookout for a female. They will descend on her and try to copulate while she vigorously signals her antipathy by moving her tail from side to side in order to dislodge the male's sexual organ. Similarly, a male scorpion, if unsuccessful in courting a partner, will take to draconian measures and simply throw himself on a passing victim, pincering her in order to adopt a mating position. As it happens, these attempted violations usually do not succeed, gentle methods of courtship tending to work best.

As with us, sexuality among animals is not invariably based on the conventional, and most common, boy-meets-girl arrangement. There is, for example, evidence that homosexuality, both male and female, exists in the wild, suggesting perhaps that a certain amount of same-sex preference is inevitable, if not necessary, in every social organization. Low-ranking male monkeys will sometimes offer their genitals for inspection by dominant males, who on occasions will even mount the subordinates. One researcher studying male manatees, those strange-looking aquatic mammals that may have given rise to ancient mermaid legends, observed what looked like mutual masturbation among male followers of a female in oestrus. A more common sight is female homosexuality among domesticated cattle, with

(*Overleaf*) Lions in Kenya. A successful mating.

85

Last of the line. This mule, a hybrid of a donkey and a Welsh pony, cannot reproduce. But it remains a useful working animal.

cows mounting each other in the absence of a bull. Gulls, too, practice lesbianism. Dr Robert Trivers has discovered long-term lesbian relationships in five species of gulls, with one of the pair showing normal 'male' behaviour such as courtship feeding, mounting and attempted copulation.

Two in one

Perhaps the most unusual sexual behaviour of all, however, is exhibited by those creatures which are effectively two sexes in one: the hermaphrodites. Hermaphrodism is rare but not unknown among humans. Some people are born with an anomalous intersexual physiology, possessing a combination of male and female reproductive organs. There are transsexuals who, by virtue of their strong sense of gender identity, choose to 'change sex', and bisexuals who are impartial in their preference for partners. And there is the transvestite or 'cross-dresser', who is only happy when wearing the clothes associated with the opposite sex.

Analogues of all these forms of behaviour, in some shape or form, are observed among animals. The wrasse fish, for example, changes sex from female to male, while the clown fish operates in the other direction, changing from male to female. The damselfly female is normally grey in colour, as opposed to the brilliant blue of the male. But certain females have adopted an appearance nearly as bright as the males, a form of transvestism. As for hermaphrodism, there is the deep sea lizard fish, living in the profound reaches of the mid-Atlantic where all life is extremely thinly spread. In such an environment heterosexual or even homosexual encounters are a problem because there are simply too few of the same species around. A lizard fish could swim for many days on end without coming across a suitable mate. Evolution has here contrived so that this species is hermaphrodite. It is both male and female, so that any meeting with another fish can be the basis of a sexual union. Similarly, the black hamlet fish, living in the tropical Atlantic, takes it in turns to play male and female with another individual of its kind. One will release a batch of eggs for fertilization by the other. Then the sexual roles will be reversed, the erstwhile father producing the eggs and vice versa.

Most hermaphrodite animals need the intervention of another like themselves to ensure fertilization. But there are a few species that are, reproductively speaking, self-contained. These fertilize themselves, despite the fact that this system has the disadvantage, in general, of producing offspring with diminished genetic variability. Examples of self-fertilizers are the killfish of the Gulf of Mexico and the freshwater snail, both of whom live in a permanently unpredictable environment where they can rely on nothing, not even the arrival of a mate.

Avoiding the wrong sort

Apart from the self-fertilizing hermaphrodites and those animals such as the virgin aphid that reproduces without sex altogether, by the process of parthenogenesis or 'virgin birth', it is essential that one species mates only with its own kind and not another. Because the different species are, by definition, organisms with a separate genetic make-up, it can literally be suicidal for two species to join, because their offspring are rarely viable. True, there are a few hybrids that are successful, up to a point, such as the mule, a cross between a male ass and a female horse. As a rule, however, a phenomenon called 'hybrid breakdown' is far more likely to occur, where either the egg and sperm fail to fuse, or, even if they do, the resultant animal is unable to mate successfully (which is the case, incidentally, with the viable but sterile mule).

Hybridization may also impair essential communication between animals. It has been demonstrated that although two American tree frogs of different species can mate, their offspring will mature to produce an ineffectual, non-distinctive hybridized mating call. Females will always prefer the call of their own species to that of the hybrid. So ultimately, deprived of opportunities to spread his seed, the male hybrid will find himself to all intents and purposes sterilized by being unable to communicate with females.

In this critical process of ensuring that a prospective partner belongs to the right species, communication plays a supremely important role. To biologists the North American grey tree frog appeared for many years to be just one species with two slightly varied calls: one a rapid trill, the other somewhat slower. But to female frogs these slight variants spell the difference between separate though related species. Experiments showed that the offspring of matings between frogs of different call-types were less likely to survive than those born of frogs with the same calls. Genetic compatibility – and incompatibility – are thus signalled quite clearly in the wild by a species-specific call.

Calling is just one means of indicating an appropriate species. Appearances, smell and courtship behaviour, as we saw in Chapter Five, all carry information from one individual to another to help in the recognition process, which is tantamount to a matching of important genetic characteristics: the animal version of the pre-marital blood test. It is astonishing how well these exchanges of information appear to work among species that are so closely related as to be, at least to outsiders such as ourselves, practically indistinguishable.

Not only do animals manage to recognize the right species, they also avoid mating with close relatives. In human societies we have long appreciated that incestuous breeding has harmful effects in mixing together a stock of genes that are too close for biological comfort. With few exceptions, incest taboos are widespread in all cultures. How, though, do animals recognize kith and kin? Among house mice, smells are extremely important in incest-avoidance, as shown by a simple experiment which one can carry out quite easily at home with pet mice.

Collect the wood shavings from the bottom of a mouse cage that is known to house the brother of a given female. Then collect some more wood shavings from the cage of another completely unrelated but familiar male. Place the female in front of the two piles and see how much time she spends sniffing at each of them. She will invariably spend more time exploring the social odours of the unrelated mouse. In such a case the sense of smell alone tells the female that this individual is an interesting mating proposition, while the other is not. Among Japanese quail, close relatives seem to indicate their presence by their physical appearance, while for some songbirds it has been shown that a female can judge relatedness by listening to a male's song. If this is too close to that of her father's, she tends to avoid the singer as a partner.

It is not always easy, however, for animals unerringly to avoid incest, any more than it might be for humans if we did not already know, as is usually the case, the identity and background of a member of the opposite sex. When male baboons or chimpanzees mature, they do not attempt to mate with their mothers, simply because females tend to spend a lot of time

Incest avoidance is extremely important. Among this closely knit population of hamadryas baboons, close relatives do not mate with each other.

with their young. There is no recognition problem. The picture may be far less clear, however, for those primate species with promiscuously inclined mothers who will have mated quite widely. It has been observed that pigtail monkeys or macaques have trouble in telling who is closely related to them on their father's side, though they are quite successful in distinguishing the maternal relatives with whom they are, on a day to day basis, more familiar.

Establishing relationships

If our animal relatives reflect some of the surprising diversity of human sexual activity, so do they, too, in their patterns of 'family life' and parental care, built as these normally are on relationships of longer duration than the comparatively swift exchanges of courtship and copulation. In fact, it is even possible to find what amounts to the animal equivalent of a 'marriage' among species such as the swan, kittiwake or albatross, which, having found a partner, remain with it for life.

Without stretching the comparisons too far, one might almost say of the hamadryas baboon that it seems to recognize the importance of the wedding as a symbolic act of union. Male hamadryas baboons appear to respect the conjugal bond between females and lesser males in the troop dominance hierarchy. They will not, as one might expect from other species where competition for mates is ferocious and tends to wreak havoc with existing pairings, attempt to steal another male's wife. They will, however, anticipate their own nuptial arrangements by adopting a young female as a kind of protegée-cum-child bride with whom they will later form a union.

Conversely, primate husbands are a jealous breed, going to great lengths to chase away any males that threaten their connubial harmony. Alternatively, the jealous husband will express his disapproval with a quasi-sexual act, attempting to 'mount' an interloper in the typical manner of a dominant asserting his higher status with a subordinate.

One mate or more?

Higamus Hogamus,
*   women are monogamous.*
Hogamus Higamus,
*   men are polygamous.*

Thus wrote the psychologist William James after this brief secret of the marital universe (or so he believed at the time) had been revealed to him in a famous dream. As with all such 'revelations', while not shatteringly profound, it contains a sizeable grain of truth. A broad general pattern among human couples establishing a long-term relationship is one man to one woman, with the female tending perhaps towards greater sexual stability and fidelity. How do we compare with other animals?

It is an interesting question because the relationships formed by animals in their mating systems are by no means a mere matter of chance, whim or fancy. They are fundamental to the whole life cycle of the organism: how it reproduces, rears its young and generally organizes its life. As a rule, monogamy is rarely practised, except among birds, where nine out of ten species have a one-to-one mating system. Birds need to keep together because an egg and a chick require a lot of parental investment in time and energy – so much so that usually both parent birds have to cooperate in providing warmth for incubation and nourishment to ensure that their offspring grows into a viable fledgling. Many small birds need to feed their young, for example, anything from four to twelve times an hour during the daytime. That means, with several nestlings to nourish, providing a catering service of hundreds of meals every day. In the face of such demands, it is in the male as well as the female interest for both parents to take joint responsibility in caring for their young. What happens more often is that a male, having fertilized a female, will go off and inseminate as many females as he can, leaving it up to each of his concubines to ensure the survival of his genes, often in his total absence.

Among mammals only about 5% of all males limit their attentions to one mate. Among fish the figure is even lower; and in other groups monogamy is virtually never practised at all. Most male animals work on the principle of 'the more offspring carrying your genes, the more successful you are in evolutionary and hence survival terms'. That being the case, researchers have become interested in the monogamous minority, asking themselves why these should practice what appears to be remarkable and paradoxical behaviour.

Dr John Mitani has concentrated some of his work on the gibbon which, along with klipspringers, marmosets, jackals (and ourselves), is one of the maritally faithful. Mated pairs of gibbons occupy permanent and exclusive ranges in the rain forests of South-east Asia. They are very vocal creatures with, as Ian Redmond describes them, 'hauntingly beautiful' whooping calls which echo through the canopy for more than half a mile, singing solo or in love duets. It had been suggested that the purpose of these calls was both to mark the joint territory and to reinforce the bond of the mated pair.

However, if a passing stray female were to venture into the range, why should the male not be opportunistic and mate with her? This was the question which Dr Mitani set out to investigate in the Kutai Game Reserve in Indonesia, where pairs of gibbons live. He did so with a series of play-back experiments in which he broadcast tape recordings of strange gibbons to two husband-and-wife teams.

He found, significantly, that if he played a female call or a male-female duet, the females in the Reserve would immediately reply to the call, soon to be joined by their mates. Each female, moreover, would make a move towards the loudspeaker from which the intruding calls issued. If, however, John Mitani played a strange male call, the gibbon 'wife' remained silent. Eventually the husband would silently wander up to the loudspeaker to 'challenge' the newcomer. It would seem, then, that the female gibbon tends to intervene by calling out herself whenever a potentially competing female makes her presence audible. But the male, too, seems keen on his steady marital state. 'Mated males,' says Dr Mitani, 'contribute to enforcing monogamy by deterring threats posed by solitary males.' Small wonder that one commentator was moved to describe the monogamous gibbons as 'high-fidelity vocalists'.

Bigamists, polygamists and harem masters

Once a year the bull elephant seal – a 4-ton monster some 20 feet (6 m) in length – forsakes the waters of the Southern Ocean or the American Pacific to drag its fattened body ashore on an isolated island. There it finds a large number of female seals who, having given birth to their pups, are now ready again for mating. In a confined area the bull is at liberty to pick and choose a fine harem of up to forty or so sexual companions. He goes from one to another, mounting them at will – provided, of course, that he has established his credentials as the dominant male. Any female will readily submit to the crushing weight of a male three times her size if he has won his spurs by seeing off the opposition in fierce fights. She will protest noisily, however, if a subordinate attempts to copulate with her. In fact, 90% of the females are fertilized by only 10% of the males, the remaining males having to be content with quick access to females while the harem master is otherwise engaged.

Superficially, the male seems to be controlling this set-up by virtue of his physical size and strength, coupled with the violence of his fighting. Yet within this polygynous mating system, the female, too, is having a say in the matter. Not only does she make her displeasure known, vocally as well as with gestures, to less-than-dominant males trying to mate with her; she also makes a lot of noise during copulation with a subordinate should this occur, attempting thereby to catch the attention of the preferred dominant male who will return to chase away other hopeful but inferior males.

Actually, female 'choice' among seals appears to be even more subtle than this. The female knows that before the males depart after the brief breeding season, she must be inseminated. But as the season wears on, even the dominant animal, worn down by constant fighting and jealous defending of his harem, becomes an unreliable source of sperm. So a female will instinctively calculate that it is better to have loved and lost than never to have loved at all. Should she not have mated earlier in the season with the dominant bull, she will allow a subordinate to father her offspring.

The process by which a female in the wild does her utmost – at least

initially – to ensure that most of her offspring are sired by the strongest, fittest male is observed time and time again. During the red deer rutting period, for example, stags compete ferociously for the attentions of females and the guardianship of a harem consisting of twenty or so members. Again, a mighty physique and the ability to use it to good advantage in a fight with competing males, is of prime importance. So too is the stag's capacity to communicate its potential supremacy with blood-curdling calls. Part of the physiological preparation for the rut is a change in the male vocal apparatus. The voice-box enlarges in order to produce booming roars that echo around the hills during the peak rutting weeks in the second half of October. It is a two-edged signal: to males for keeping them at bay; to females for reminding them of their continued wisdom in choice of partner. Before a harem keeper is challenged physically by another male, he is first challenged vocally. If an intruder can outroar the incumbent or merely equal him, the chances are that there will be a close fight to decide the matter.

So often is mate selection determined by the female choosing a physically strong male – one that will give her sons and daughters desirable bodily characteristics – that some psychologists have speculated as to whether something akin to this might be operating among humans. Their argument runs along these lines. At earlier periods of human evolution, it was important for the male to be swift of foot, hard of muscle and keen of eye in order to bring home the family's meal. Nowadays, superficially at least, the need for muscle has been replaced by the virtue of brains. Mr Average does not have to stalk game on the savannah, but succeed in that other kind of jungle, his work, in order to satisfy the family requirements. However, going to work, using machines, living in towns and cities are all very recent patterns of behaviour, measured in evolutionary time. Perhaps, argue some, we carry with us still some of those instincts that dictated the lives of our remote

Lord and master. The northern elephant seal in the company of his female entourage.

Roar of the red deer stag.

ancestors, including their sexual activities.

In short, do women, when they are attracted to men, look at what they say they look at (the crinkle of the eyes, the neatness of the suit, the friendliness of the demeanour, and so on)? Or are they really looking for wide shoulders, slim hips and deep chests, all features consistent with a successful hunter of the plains?

This is a hotly debated topic because if the answer is 'yes', then perhaps some of the more extravagant claims of socio-biologists might be given support. If 'no', how does one explain the experiments carried out by Dr Glenn Wilson of the Institute of Psychiatry in London, which recorded the body zones scanned by the eyes of women when meeting men at social gatherings? True to the socio-biological prediction, females seem to be far more interested in buttocks, chests and shoulders than in faces and subtleties of expression.

Sexual cycles

A very important element in successful mating and reproduction is timing. Both partners have to be sexually ready for their act of union if it is to enable them to increase their numbers. Just as we humans have sexual cycles, the principal one being the monthly ebb and flow of female hormones that regulate fertility and menstruation, so, too, do animals. There are good and bad times for mating, fertile and barren phases. In regulating and synchronizing copulation for optimum results, communication once more looms very large indeed.

Take the female elephant seals, all simultaneously ready on their islands to be inseminated by the dominant males. It is no coincidence that all the females are on oestrus at precisely the same time of year. Even more remarkable is the female lion – and here we might well make a comparison with ourselves – which, unlike the seal, does not come into oestrus at any particular time of the year. However, all the lionesses in the pride come on heat in synchrony. This means that when they are in oestrus there is always an abundance of receptive females available for mating: males do not have to queue up for the favours of one female at a time. In these instances there appear to be subtle interactions between females to bring their breeding periods or phases of sexual receptivity into close harmony. A similar effect has been observed in laboratory mice. If a group of females are kept together in a cage and a male then introduced, the females' oestrus cycles immediately become synchronized. This curious phenomenon – the so-called 'Whitten Effect' has also been noted among women such as nuns who live together in a tightly knit convent environment. Prolonged cohabitation brings their hormonal behaviour into fairly close coordination.

No one knows for certain how these effects are produced but clearly this type of synchronous behaviour must involve some communication between individuals. Among our mammal relatives it would be reasonable to suggest that internal, hormonal secretions are somehow advertised externally by means of pheronomes. Perhaps the same is true of sexually synchronized humans.

Female oestrous cycles may be influenced, too, by the behaviour of males. In India the langur monkey sometimes lives in troops consisting of several females, their young and a single male. If a new male is successful in ousting the incumbent, he will often kill the young in the troop, thereby encouraging the females to come into oestrus more quickly than they would otherwise have done. Similar oestrous acceleration takes place among lions, where again the challenging male will resort to infanticide in order to make his new mates sexually receptive more rapidly.

Males, too, need to time their sexual activities. With stags or seals there is a fixed seasonal period in the year. But with the elephant the equivalent to the rutting period – the 'musth' – is unsynchronized, each male coming into musth at a different time of the year. Being in musth has rather dramatic effects on the dominance patterns among elephants; and since their periods are unsynchronized, such patterns among male elephants are in a constant state of flux, depending on who is in musth and for how long. Younger and lower-ranking males stay in musth for only a few days at a time but among older individuals this breeding period may last for as long as three or four months.

Dr Joyce Poole, a researcher into elephant musth behaviour, says that there is a close relationship between the male's fighting behaviour, his success in guarding oestrous females and his musth state, along with other factors such as the levels of the male hormone testosterone in his bloodstream. Given the asynchrony of musth, this means that 'males must continually monitor one another to assess fighting ability'. And that, in turn, according to Dr Poole, means that male elephants have to make judgments about other males, based on various kinds of information received. Among these channels of communication are those low-pitched rumbles which we came across earlier. Dr Poole, while working with Katherine Payne, the scientist who first detected these unsuspected sounds, identified one such low-frequency call as the 'musth rumble'.

Male elephants in musth also communicate their state by other means. Joyce Poole and Cynthia Moss, working in the Amboseli National Park in Kenya, observed a condition among older males which they termed 'green penis syndrome'. The bulls would continuously drip urine, accompanied by a strong odour, from a fungus-covered penis. There were a few other characteristic phenomena, especially copious secretions from the temporal glands, aggressive behaviour and more time than usual spent by males in the company of females. One further point of interest in Poole and Moss's work is that it took place in Kenya, so establishing that musth does indeed occur in the African elephant. Until that time musth had only been recognized among Asiatic elephants.

Who looks after the children?

Among the changes taking place in contemporary human society is the gradual but discernible emergence of the 'New Man'. Unlike the majority of his sex, this new type of male, it is said, is a softer, more caring individual, concerned about the qualitative and emotional side of life. Instead of being a macho-type breadwinner, leaving the day-to-day upbringing of the children to the wife, he is making a deliberate attempt to share in her traditional 'female' role, even to the extent in extreme instances, of staying at home to look after the children while she goes out to work.

Such examples of truly shared parenthood are decidedly rare among humans, at least in the Western world, but not so among many of our animal relatives, where male care is commonplace. Many animals exercise no parental care at all, notably fish species which, having laid their eggs, leave them to the tides of fortune. But when fish do care for their young, it is usually the concern of the male, especially where the eggs are fertilized externally, i.e. outside the mother's body.

The male stickleback builds a weed nest as a nursery for the newly laid eggs where he can swish fresh water over them to keep them aerated, remove parasites and keep an eye open for predators, including cannibalistic members of the same species. The male seahorse becomes even more involved in the process. He has evolved a special pouch in his belly for carrying eggs transferred from the female. In this organ he fertilizes them and protects them up to the moment of birth, almost like a surrogate womb.

Patterns of human parental care can vary quite widely among human families living next door to one another, and the same is true of two species of fish, namely the triggerfish of the Red Sea. In his observations of two triggerfish species in the underwater laboratory of Neritica in Eilat, Israel, on the Gulf of Akaba, Dr Hans Fricke found a 'curious difference' in their surprisingly distinct behaviours. Both species live in coral reefs where their eggs are externally fertilized; but in one species the females alone tend the eggs, whereas in the other, both parents share the task. In the latter case the male, though not fanning the eggs, will help defend them against interlopers, while males of the former species appear to take no interest at all in the welfare of mother and young. The reason remains unclear. Theoretically,

one would expect a male to try to protect the eggs that he has fertilized within his territory. Yet on the contrary, the brood-caring female even reacts aggressively towards her mate and tries to drive him off if he approaches.

Male elephant in musth: secretions ooze from swollen temporal glands and the erect penis.

Equally puzzling to biologists is the tendency for some animals to invest precious energy in the care of young that are not their own. It is hard to see what evolutionary purpose is served by expending effort on someone else's offspring, thereby limiting the resources available for the care and development of one's own. Dr Tim Halliday describes this phenomenon of assisting the breeding activities of others as a major challenge to the evolutionary theorist. Whatever the reason, however, this apparently 'altruistic' behaviour in the care and welfare of the young, and sometimes its mother, undoubtedly takes place. It occurs among the hunting dogs of Africa where caring for the young is a matter of collective concern. We see it, too, among primates where an unrelated baby-minder will look after a youngster, sometimes acting as a temporary foster-parent, sometimes as a more permanent adoptive parent. Sarah Blaffer Hrdy of Harvard University admits that such conspecific care is puzzling because, although a primate may assume the role of uncle or aunt, there is not necessarily any genetic link between the carer and the cared-for. So what are the advantages for the animal which offers care and protection to someone else's offspring?

Dr Hrdy has catalogued several examples of such behaviour in attempting to answer this central question. She has uncovered instances among Japanese macaques, chimpanzees and langurs of adult males protecting and rescuing youngsters; and so has another researcher, Dumond, who watched a young adult male squirrel monkey approach very close to retrieve a baby

Maternal care: the female brown triggerfish fans her eggs. Males of this species take no part in looking after the brood.

Childminding in Rwanda. Early in its life an infant mountain gorilla is cared for by its mother. Later on, relatives will lend a hand.

which it thought threatened by his presence. Another related behaviour among primates is baby-sitting. In the absence of its mother, a young anubis baboon will be left in the company of an older male for up to thirty minutes at a time, several times a day, even though he happens to be the present consort of the female, not the child's father.

Sometimes orphan baboons, chimps and macaques will find a new home with a male that adopts them for good, even though the child may be sick as well as parentless. With adoption, however, in those cases studied, it seems that the caring adult is usually related to the youngster, often an older brother or sister – a simple case, apparently, of blood being thicker than water. But there is still no explanation of the 'aunting' of the young by unrelated adults. Why do some adult females act as mothers to someone else's children? Perhaps it is a kind of preparation for parenthood. Female vervets, chimps and macaques appear to make more competent mothers if they have had some practice with other youngsters before the birth of their first child. This seems to be the conclusion from various studies of animals in the wild, as well as in captivity, such as that carried out by Jane van Lawick-Goodall who found that inexperienced captive chimpanzee mothers are afraid of their firstborn, refusing to touch them or allow them to cling. Aunting, therefore, may be a vital experience for future child-bearers, a natural system for acquiring maternal skills.

Sadly, not all non-parental child-adult relationships are of benefit to

both parties. Many primate species are known to exploit other animals' children, sometimes to the point of harming them. There is, for instance, what is termed 'agonistic buffering', whereby a child is used as a means of warding off an attack from an aggressive male. Male chimps will seldom attack a female with an infant on her back. The child seems to act as a powerful signal to inhibit aggression. So an adult chimp will grab a youngster in an attempt to get safe conduct through potentially dangerous territory. Similarly, a male baboon or macaque will use a child to get close to another dominant male that he would not normally dare to approach. Again the youngster seems to serve as a signal, this time to facilitate social interactions between males – a kind of calling card; but it may be treated very badly in the process, being roughly pushed and pulled by one male or the other during their association. Another stratagem is for a male to associate with the young of a troop in order to gain entry into that community – the child this time functioning as a form of social visa.

Carried to extremes, child exploitation among primates can lead to injury, even death. Males may attack and kill the child of another male in order to increase their own chances of reproductive success while reducing those of a competitor. After bitter fights between groups of langur monkeys, the victors may kill the youngsters of the vanquished troop in an orgy of infanticide. Even this, however, is not a gratuitous act of assassination, but an example of well-adapted, evolutionary, sensible behaviour. It does, in fact, help to ensure that the females come into oestrus more quickly and are thereby ready to mate with the newcomers.

Family   harmony ...

Nevertheless, family life among animals is not all blood and thunder; far from it. For those of us who may be cynical about the quality of human parent-child relationships, there are some heartening models among even our more 'primitive' animal relatives, as, for instance, the Nile crocodile. The mother crocodile takes an enormous amount of care with her newborn. She carefully digs a nest in a river bank in which to lay her eggs, up to ninety at a time. But the eggs cannot hatch, nor can the young even leave the nest, without the mother's help. So they begin to signal to her by chirping from inside the shell, whereupon she breaks it open and carries some of the hatchlings in a special pouch, located on the floor of her mouth, to the river. There she leaves one batch and returns to the nest for another, all the while maintaining family cohesion with a series of calls which are answered by the youngsters still in the nest, as they stridently indicate their presence and their desire to be dug out. Whenever she places a fresh group alongside those youngsters in the water, she emits another gentler sound like the call of a cricket. This is a sign of contact and recognition, an acknowledgement that they belong to her. It is all very reminiscent of the familiar domestic chicken. Here, too, hen and chicks are highly vocal, always exchanging sounds, especially when danger threatens, and always maintaining tight family cohesion.

Not that parent animals necessarily have to make sounds to establish family ties. Mere presence appears to be enough to form unshakable child-parent bonds. One mechanism that operates without vocal language is that of imprinting. When a duckling or gosling, for example, hatches from the egg, the first adult it sees is its solicitous mother. Thereafter the young duck or goose seems to be indelibly stamped with the crucial, life-sustaining

information that this adult is indeed its source of food and comfort. There is no more vivid demonstration of this than the sight (recorded on film) of the ethologist Konrad Lorenz walking by a lake followed by a tidy file of young goslings, all of which had been imprinted by Lorenz who had usurped their natural mother's role at hatching. So powerful is this imprinting process that it overrides the gross physical differences between Mother Duck and Professor Lorenz, let alone the fact that they belong, of course, to two utterly different species.

Nile crocodile: mother and child.

Imprinting doubtless takes place between human babies and their mothers, as an evolutionarily necessary feature of infant development. Watch a young mother with her newborn and, apart from the encouraging cooing and laughing generated by the adoring parent, you will notice a great deal of mutual gazing. Both parties are communicating in this way. The baby is not just passively receiving the attentions of its parent but itself sending out powerful bonding signals, telling its mother: 'This is your child. Love, care and protect.'

Another non-verbal route to close relationships between parent and child – and indeed among adults – is grooming, that earnest scratching, combing, smoothing and assorted petting that occupies so much of the time of primates in close proximity. Among monkeys, there is a certain amount of grooming between individuals not very closely related, but the general pattern is for it to be directed at parents, offspring and siblings. It is a bit like the 'in' family joke or custom, which can be shared with outsiders but is originally intended to reaffirm the cohesion of the family unit. In this important ritual fingers are normally used for picking at and parting the fur of another individual; but lemurs have evolved a 'toothcomb' in their lower teeth as a specialized social organ for grooming purposes. The groomer's reward may be to be groomed in return, or perhaps receive a more tangible offering in the form of a tasty speck of salt exuded in sweat.

...and   discord

No matter how many channels of communication exist for maintaining relationships within the family, whether human or animal, there are often moments of parent-child conflict. Dr Robert Trivers has for years been collecting examples of this, starting from his observations of free-living pigeons in Cambridge, Massachusetts. A chick, at the beginning of its life, is usually treated very caringly by its parents. But this early period of solicitude gives way to what Dr Trivers calls 'more ambivalent relationships', and finally to a time when the former loving mother seeks to avoid her offspring altogether.

On his subsequent travels in India and East Africa, Dr Trivers saw some dramatic cases of parent-child conflict among langur monkeys and baboons; the infants begging with cries for milk from the mother and retaliating fiercely if rebuffed. Should mother deny her child a piggy-back ride, again there is friction and squabbling. A team of biologists led by Judy Stamps of the University of California found evidence of conflict, too, among budgerigars, mostly determined, it appears, by the tendency of the offspring to beg for too much food – behaving like greedy, selfish children making unreasonable demands on their parents.

The good news, according to Dr Stamps, is that although researchers are keenly interested in trying to determine the biological function of parent-child conflict, such behaviour is comparatively rare in nature. There is thus no overriding law or principle to dictate that all children will or should come into conflict with their parents in the course of normal family life.

A lesson from Universe 133

'Universe 133' is a four-level mouse cage, 20 feet (6 m) wide, at the American National Institute of Mental Health in Bethesda, Maryland. It contains eight cells of equal size with food and water dispensers, forming the living space for 16 groups of 12 adult mice – a total population of 192 animals. This, at least, is the optimum figure. But the researchers at NIMH wanted to find out what the effects on the mice would be if their numbers went beyond this. So they allowed the population to grow, all the while continuing to provide them with food, water and good hygienic conditions. The mice mated, produced a second generation, then a third and so on, until the density was such that the mice could not interact with one another normally, so crowded was their shrinking universe.

Mating eventually ceased altogether, so that the numbers fell precipitously from a peak of nearly 1600 mice. The mice, it seemed, were simply failing to develop mating relationships. What is more, the behaviours necessary for the parental care of the young were likewise extinguished by overcrowding. Normally good mothers became neglectful. If these effects can tell us anything about human population patterns, as the researcher in charge of the project, psychologist John B. Calhoun, thinks they might, then they represent an important warning. We too are expanding our population at an alarming rate. We too are cramming our little universe with bodies. Will we

The language of grooming. A mother emperor penguin in the Antarctic nibbles and pets the head of her chick, strengthening the parent–infant bond.

similarly reach a point where this growth trend goes into reverse? If so, will it be because overcrowding impairs those natural behaviours that drive us to mate and to look after our young?

What Dr Calhoun fears is not so much a stifling of our parental instincts by overcrowding as an impairment of the adaptability and creativity that enable us to cope with the demands of a rapidly changing world. And this too could be catastrophic. Whatever the outcome, the message is clear. Limit growth before it limits us.

Languages of Survival

'Ladies and gentlemen. I have here an ordinary pocket handkerchief. Nothing in it, see. I place it over this tumbler of water. And when I take it off again ... so, there in the glass is a gold coin. Pure magic! Thank you.' Of course, it is not magic at all, any more than sawing the lady in half or producing a billiard ball from behind your left ear are magical phenomena. We all know that the stage magician is a skilled practitioner in the showbiz arts of illusion and deception. He is inveigling us into believing one thing while he does another. And he achieves his triumphant ends by means of a good deal of subtly delivered messages full of false trails, camouflage and diversionary tactics. Yes, our conjurer is certainly an adept communicator, well versed in the language of deception.

Human acts of deception may be entertaining, like the make-believe world of the theatre, or harmless, like a tiny white lie told to protect a friend. Conversely, deception may be a serious, even deadly affair: the housebreaker posing as an electricity meter inspector; the professional con-man perpetrating an elaborate sting which may involve innocent members of the public; the child molester stopping his car to ask the trusting infant for street directions.

Deception can be turned to useful ends. During World War II land-mines were disguised as cow-pats – on the assumption that a foot soldier would automatically step round them but an enemy vehicle would blithely drive over them. More subtle was the trick used by the US Government which published a special issue of *National Geographic* magazine illustrating the insignia and numbers of the various branches of the US armed services. The published statistics contained a sprinkling of truth and a great deal of falsehood, so as to provide the enemy with a very misleading picture. Purporting to be what one is not, in word, deed or appearance; employing clever ruses that play on the 'psychology' of the target; manipulating through pretence – these are all commonplace in our species. Again, we are not alone.

Many faces of deception

We have thus far seen many ways in which animals communicate, spreading information in order to influence the behaviour of others: how, for example, the male displays to the female during courtship in order to get her to select him for a mate. Dr Robert Trivers stresses, however, that such information may not necessarily be genuine. 'One of the most important things to realize about systems of animal communication,' he writes, 'is that they are not systems for the dissemination of the truth.' In the natural world there is a constant twofold struggle going on in every organism: to eat without being eaten, and to ensure that one's genes are passed on to succeeding generations. Under these twin pressures, evolution will contrive any strategy likely to give

Visual deception: the spiny bug of South Africa.

an animal the edge in either of these objectives. And evolution shows no compunction in using dishonest tactics if these can confer the critical advantages.

Thus, as we shall see, animals will often use deception to capture their prey, exhibiting thereby a range of wiles and ruses that makes the most adept human political schemer look positively crude. Similarly, they will go to great lengths to trick a predator into leaving them alone, making themselves appear less attractive as a menu item than they really are. Or, finally, an animal will adopt some quite astonishing strategies to bring about that all-important union with another of the same species. Love, or at least the drive to mate and reproduce, will certainly find a way.

Disappearing acts

The simplest form of deception in order to avoid predation is camouflage. The animal merges into the background because its protective coloration, and sometimes its form, mimic those of the immediate environment. Like the greens and beiges of the soldier's battledress, these deceitful colours are communicating misinformation. The bird predator scanning the canopy of a tree perceives only the expected clusters of leaves, missing the insects that are virtually indistinguishable from the foliage.

Camouflage works in a variety of ways. The chameleon changes its skin colouring to harmonize with its background; and the chameleon prawn can vary its hue from brown to red to green (especially when swimming among sea lettuce) during the day, taking an appropriate pale blue tinge at night. Butterflies and moths often have colours and textures that make them indistinguishable from a leaf or tree bark, as does the Malaysian flying gecko which, when flattened and immobile on a tree trunk, is virtually impossible to pick out.

Of course, even with these so-called 'passive' forms of camouflage, animals need to choose the right backgrounds against which to merge, and indeed to adopt an appropriate bodily orientation. Take the bark-resting moths of North America. About thirty or so species of these moths have brown, grey or whitish forewings, shaded in intricate patterns, and masking the more lavishly coloured hindwings when at rest. It would be counter-productive for these moths to place themselves on a bark background in such a way that their marking patterns go one way, say at right angles to the trunk, while the lines of the bark itself stretch out vertically. A predator would soon interpret this unnatural chess-board-style cross-hatching as worthy of investigation. Thus the language of camouflage can only function correctly when properly employed.

The forces of evolution have gone even further in shaping the appearance of creatures such as the stick insect, which resembles its habitat in both colour and form. There are, in fact, about 2000 species of stick insects, mostly tropical, and mostly feeding on leaves, stems and sometimes flowers. These highly effective animals are able to freeze suddenly at the approach of trouble, and such is their resemblance to the surrounding vegetation that your eye can lose them if you glance away for a short time. Even the eggs of stick insects have in-built camouflage, tending to resemble small seeds.

It is inevitable that even an animal as good at hiding itself as the stick insect must from time to time be spotted and attacked. When this happens there can be a quite startling change of visual tactic, from the self-effacing to self-advertising. One species will grab at a predator with the front legs and curl its abdomen upwards, very like the scorpion, thus mimicking a particularly intimidating organism. Another species rapidly unfurls its wings to expose extremely bright underwing colours, rather like certain moths.

(*Overleaf*) Imitation for survival. The green stick insect of Costa Rica.

Hawk moth, lost against the bark texture of the Mopane tree.

107

This unexpected display is sufficient to distract the predator for those precious instants that the stick insect needs to take flight.

For camouflage to be effective, it is usually necessary for the self-protecting animal to remain still. The young gazelle is particularly adept at staying immobile for hours on end. Even so, this may not work, because animals, as we have seen, can loudly betray their presence by the evocative language of body odours. So the gazelle contrives both to store its waste products until it gets on the move, and to refrain from emitting any tell-tale scents that might waft into the nose of an odour-sensitive predator.

Mimicry: an active form of camouflage

The camouflage used by many animals is designed not so much to hide as to misrepresent. Thus the harmless hoverfly, with conspicuous black and yellow coloration that mimics that of the bee or wasp, appears to be a ferocious fighter. The crab spider mimics not other animal species but plants, in order to catch prey. Sitting motionless on a flower, its colours and patterns exactly matching those of its background, the spider has only to wait for its next meal to arrive in the form of nectar-feeding bees, butterflies and hoverflies. At the same time, of course, the crab spider is keeping itself out of harm's way, remaining invisible to its own predators. Protective coloration also confers a double-edged benefit to some species of tropical flower mantids, relatively large creatures in pink and white, with leg segments shaped in broad curves that match those of flower petals.

There are many variants on the wolf in sheep's clothing phenomenon. Some tropical spiders are almost identical in appearance to the ants on which they feed. This close resemblance, combined with the spider's ability to lull the ant into a state of complacency and compliance by gently stroking its antennae, has provided many a welcome meal. Meanwhile, overhead, the tropical zone-tailed hawk, with the same silhouette and soaring, gliding flight as the vulture, constantly deceives small mammals into thinking that, like the vulture, it is an exclusive carrion eater. To their cost they find that the hawk enjoys live game.

Another form of deception by mimicry is that named after a contemporary of Charles Darwin, the celebrated English naturalist Henry Walter Bates, who carried out extensive observations on the exotic butterflies of the Amazon forests. Bates found that there were brightly coloured but patently unpalatable species of butterfly flying around among similar-looking but savoury species. He suggested that the latter were being protected by the former by virtue of physical resemblance, even though the species were unrelated. This so called Batesian mimicry, based on the fact that many animals are poisonous, venomous or just plain evil to taste, can be seen in hoverflies that mimic stinging bees; viceroy butterflies that mimic the highly unpalatable monarch species; black flycatcher birds that may mimic the tropical drongo with its reputedly unpleasant-tasting flesh; the African rufous flycatcher which resembles the ant thrush, thought to taste nasty because the latter's diet of ants makes its flesh redolent of formic acid; and the salamander which is refused by predators that have already had the doubtful pleasure of tasting the red and black North American newt.

There is a further refinement on this kind of defensive strategy, named after the 19th-century German zoologist Fritz Muller, and called, logically enough, Mullerian mimicry. Here both species are unpalatable, either because they are distasteful or harmful, and they, too, resemble each other closely. In this way individuals, by associating with other unpalatable species, increase their own chances of staying out of harm's way. It is really Batesian mimicry stepped up a gear.

Aide-mémoire mimicry

Yet a further variation on the Batesian theme of making oneself unpleasant to taste or harmful to an aggressor is what Dr Miriam Rothschild calls 'aide-mémoire mimicry'. 'There are a number of animals and plants,' writes Dr Rothschild, 'which gain protection from predators by subtly reminding them of an unpleasant experience connected with predation.' Thus the buzzing of a drone fly appears to make her own pet dog recall an unpleasant experience it must have had with a honeybee. No sooner does an autumnal drone fly appear on the scene than the deceived animal 'retires discreetly under the table'. She goes on to relate a number of analogous instances: a beetle which makes a squeaky buzzing like a drowsy bumblebee when attacked; a moth that bears no resemblance at all to a stinging insect but manages to suggest that terrifying prospect by virtue of a characteristic, hornet-like buzz; even a plant that has little appendages that look like slugs or snails to would-be predators.

Appearances can be deceptive. The lower insect is a fly mimicking the colours and form of the wasp above it. This is an effective disguise against predation.

The false stare of the saturnid moth. Wings open to reveal intimidating eye spots on the male below. The female's wings are closed (above).

Underwater scene-shifter. The spiney spider crab camouflaged with red weed which it has planted on its own carapace.

Props and other paraphernalia

Props are often used in order to deceive. These may either be naturally evolved features of an animal's own body or 'borrowed' accoutrements from its habitat. One of the best-known instances in the first category is the use some insects make of eye-spot patterns; butterflies, in particular, have large staring 'eyes' on their wings that seem to deter some of their bird predators. In the course of a trip to Australia, Professor Tom Eisner, of Cornell University, an authority on insect communication systems, began to wonder whether this commonly observed form of deterrence might be exploited for the comfort of the human population. He had arrived during the starling breeding season, that time of the year when thousands of starlings make themselves a considerable nuisance to people out and about, especially joggers, some of whom have even been attacked by aggressive birds. If eye-spots on insects deter birds, might they do the same if attached, say, to the hat of a jogger?

Accordingly, Tom Eisner painted a pair of large staring eyes on his baseball cap and set out for a run. Not one starling flew near him. A hypothesis vindicated, he thought. However, on subsequent days he went jogging without his cap and, again, no starling attacks. So perhaps it was not such a good idea after all. As a home experiment you might attempt this yourself in a modified form. Try painting a large pair of eyes on a hat and seeing what effect, if any, this appears to have on your neighbourhood birds when

you wear it. You may conclude that perhaps the old-fashioned scarecrow ought to be replaced by something more like the ocular 'keep off' sign that has kept countless butterflies alive in the face of their natural enemies!

Intimidating eye-spots are also found on frogs, such as one South American species which, if it does not succeed in frightening off an aggressor, has an auxiliary system in the form of unpleasant odours secreted by glands in the region of the eye spots. These, incidentally, are on its backside.

Moving up in the scale of sophistication, we meet the Bolas spider, another trickster with a subtle line in props. The spider spins a gossamer strand, at the end of which is a sticky globule impregnated with a chemical that mimics perfectly the sexual scent of a common local moth. The apparatus acts as a powerful lure. Moths are attracted to the globule and become stuck, whereupon the spider hauls in its baited lasso and devours its prey.

Perhaps an even more surprising form of deception is that of the spider crab which has something of the extravagant actor in its make-up, using props and scenery in an elaborate plot to stay alive in the coastal waters that form its stage. These ingenious crabs decorate their bodies with living sponges, algae and barnacles in the effort to camouflage themselves. Once on the crab's carapace, however, these living ornaments take hold and continue to grow, forming a totally realistic micro-ecology. As a bonus, some of the sponges are distasteful so that, if its cover is blown, the spider crab has another line of defence.

This is not the only maritime creature to use whatever comes to hand in its surroundings to misinform would-be predators. Some gastropod molluscs off the coast of Florida decorate themselves with the empty shells of bivalves, carefully cementing each one in place with a naturally secreted substance and continuing this painstaking pretence until every gap is filled and the mollusc is able to merge with the sea bed – shells and all. The converse of this strategy is seen in a species of orb-weaver spider which, instead of trying to merge into its surroundings, endeavours to modify them for camouflage purposes. It will spin on the web two little dense areas of gossamer that could be mistaken for its own body – another example of diversionary architecture.

Bluff and more bluff

If the bodies of animals are not always what they seem to be to the eye of predator, prey or mate, nor are the signals they emit, be these audio, visual or pheromonal. In the great days of vaudeville and music hall there was invariably someone on the bill who did animal 'impressions', including birdsong. But animals themselves are often skilled actors in the theatre of deception, adept at reproducing the sounds of other species.

Faced with the unwelcome prospect of being hunted, the dormouse is capable of hissing like a snake to deter attacks. Conversely, there is the semaphore strategy of the female firefly, who remains immobile on vegetation and makes herself known to males in the vicinity by her flashing sequences. But, as noted in Chapter Five, females of one genus of American firefly – *Photuris* – will flash at the passing males of another genus called *Photinus*. When the males approach, lured by the siren-call of these *femmes fatales*, the deceptive *Photuris* female seizes and devours her prey: a graphic example of a consuming passion.

Most examples of this kind of deception, as observed by scientists over the years, take place between different species. Yet there are a few cases of

Web of deception. The orb-building spider sometimes spins her web where it will become scattered with seeds or other plant matter. This acts both to deter passing birds from flying through the laboriously constructed web and to disguise the spider from prey.

Playing dead. Eyes staring and mouth gaping, the grass snake feigns death.

deceit within a species. Rick Steger and Roy Caldwell of the University of California, Berkeley, showed that a Caribbean species of marine crustacean, a stomatopod called *Gonodactylus bredini*, tricks opponents of the same species by the use of bluff. After moulting, these stomatopods temporarily lose their body armour and the use of the raptorial organs specially designed for seizing prey. Thus they are very vulnerable and likely to be evicted from the holes in which they live by others of their kind.

However, if attacked by a squatter, the newly moulted animal behaves as it would if it were between moults: it defends its cavity by a special display, leaning out of its home, facing its opponent and laterally spreading its claws. It is the conventional language of threat and aggression, like the rattle of sabre or shield, even though the creature is really in no shape to fight. Bluffed by the visual signal, the would-be attacker recoils in a defensive posture or swims away. Should it call the bluff and continue to intrude, the incumbent invariably backs down and gives up its cavity.

The histrionic skill of this particular crustacean finds many echoes in interactions between different species. The cleaner wrasse is a fish that lives in the coral reefs of the Pacific and Indian Oceans where it forms a symbiotic relationship with larger fish, cleaning off their parasites and dead skin. 'Customers' of this cleaner fish tolerate its presence as it provides a natural valet service, while the cleaner thrives on the organisms infesting its patrons. However, there is another fish, a blenny, that strongly resembles the cleaner wrasse in coloration but not in occupation. The blenny swims in the same waters, looking for all the world like a cleaner. But a 'client' will be relieved of more than its parasites as the blenny's sabre teeth rip into it and tear off a chunk of fin or tail.

An animal can often save itself by acting as if dead or injured. Beetles, grasshoppers, mantids, spiders and snakes may all become absolutely motionless for a short while if attacked. So, too, will moth species such as the European pale prominent moth, which has the added advantage of being coloured in such a way as to look like a lifeless wood shaving. Thus a predator seeing the moth regards it as inanimate and therefore ignores it on the grounds that it is probably inedible.

Many predators, such as cats, will only attack living animals. Indeed, they have to kill before they feed. Thus the North American opossum, pretending to be dead – 'playing possum' – deters some, though not all, enemies.

Certain ground-nesting birds, such as the ostrich or plover, frequently put on astonishing performances in order to protect their nests. As a predator approaches a plover's nest, the mother bird will flutter lopsidedly across the ground, pretending to have a broken wing. It is an impressive show, certainly enough to distract the aggressor's attentions away from the defenceless young.

Deception in reproduction

Sigh no more, ladies, sigh no more,
Men were deceivers ever;
One foot in the sea, and one on the shore,
To one thing constant never.

Much Ado About Nothing

Distraction display of the killdeer plover. Wings dropped as if broken, the mother bird tries to deflect the attentions of a predator interested in her young.

Shakespeare's cynical generalization about sexual deception in men may well be valid. Among other animals, although it is often males that trick their way through courtship, mating and breeding, there are a few instances where females, too, are guilty of such deeds. Consider, for example, the female cuckoo. She is a brood parasite, compelled to lay her eggs in the nest of a reed warbler, hedge sparrow or any one of a number of other species of small bird. In order that her eggs be accepted in the alien nest, the female has evolved an effective method of disguise. Her eggs exactly match in coloration and size those of the unwitting – and unwilling – host bird. Each cuckoo lays only one type of egg, expressly designed for one type of foster home. An egg laid in the wrong nest or with poor matching coloration will soon be thrown out. The cuckoo, however, usually gets it right, consistently outsmarting the host mother, who is left to pay the large energy bill run up by the cuckoo's rapidly developing offspring.

Another deceptive female has been studied by Dr Hugh Robertson of Wisconsin University in a small pond near Lake Placid in Florida. On this stretch of water lives a species of damselfly in which almost one-third of the females mimic the appearance of males. But what is the function of these transvestite flies? Damselfly adults only live for a few days, during which time their mating is intensive and prolonged, lasting on average some three hours. However, although the males are anxious to mate as frequently as possible, the females are not so enthusiastic because they need to spend a certain amount of their available time feeding and bringing more eggs to maturity.

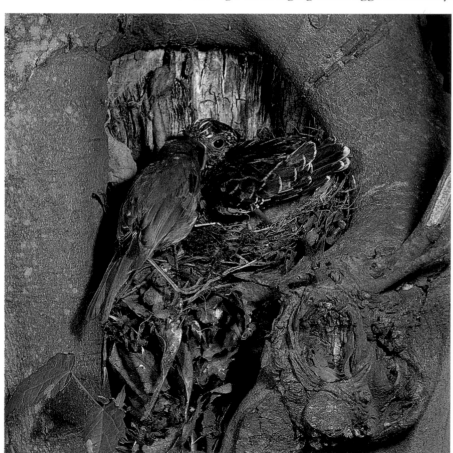

Survival of the fattest. A young cuckoo, having ousted the eggs of the host robin, is fed assiduously by the duped foster-mother.

118

Once fertilized, the females want to get on with the task of laying eggs, not copulating. Moreover, a copulating pair of flies is somewhat conspicuous to predators. So there are many reasons why a female should want to avoid repeated matings.

By mimicking the male, a female can reduce the amount of unwanted attention she receives from the opposite sex. That, at least, is Dr Robertson's explanation. But, as if often the case, it does not answer all questions about the unusual reproduction patterns of the damselfly. How, for example, does the transvestite female manage to attract a mate when she does want one? Secondly, it has been observed that egg-laying females will sometimes get trapped by water tension and drown, unless a male comes along to act as lifeguard. If he does, he usually mates with the female in his care. But a male would not choose to rescue what appears to be another male. So transvestism here could be suicidal.

Manipulative males

Cases of female deception for sexual ends are relatively few in the broad perspective of animal mating behaviour. For the most part, true to Shakespeare's suggestion, the male is the guilty party. The male ten-spined stickleback fish is another transvestite. During spawning, females of the species often group together in one nest. Indeed, the males welcome as many spawning females into their midst as they can muster, thereby gaining access to a greater number of eggs to fertilize. However, sometimes a pseudo-female will arrive – actually a male but with the drab coloration of a female. The host male, although it already has one female and her clutch in the nest, lets in the newcomer, expecting 'her' obligingly to lay another clutch of eggs for him to fertilize. Instead, the disguised male fertilizes the first clutch in the nest, cuckolding the original 'husband'.

An odd variant on the theme of male transvestism occurs in the red-sided garter snake which mates in writhing balls of animals, each female being courted by many males, sometimes in a ratio of 1 to 100. In the course of their research into the behaviour of garter snakes, Robert Mason and David Crews of the University of Texas came across an extraordinary phenomenon. In many of these mating swarms there are sometimes no females at all. Instead, several males appear to pay court to an individual male – a 'she-male' – rubbing their chins along its back as the characteristic preliminary to copulation. The she-males are identical in appearance to normal males but, as Mason and Crews discovered, they do secrete a pheromone that mimics the attractant chemical of a true female. So these pseudo-males appear to be employing female scents in order to seduce normal males. Yet the story does not end there.

The motivation for this form of deception is not, as one might at first sight infer, homosexual in nature. On the contrary, studies of mating behaviour reveal that she-males actually have more success in their matings with normal females than do the unscented males. When males and she-males were allowed experimentally to court an attractive female simultaneously, the success rate of the she-males was twice as high as that of the other males. So it looks as if the male red garter snake's mimicry (in those individuals practising this form of deception) gives it an edge in heterosexual competition. It may have to seduce another male in the process, but by enticing competitors away from a real female, scores in the end.

Undoubtedly, one of the most cunning male deceivers of all is the great reed warbler, a marshland bird that constantly manages to trick a number of females into mating with it each season, contrary to the monogamous pattern found in the majority of other bird species. The great reed warbler has two strings to his polygynous bow, both based on communicating misinformation to prospective mates.

Approach number one is a deceptive display of material wealth in the form of an appealing territory. As a migrant species with a relatively short breeding season, the reed warbler needs to mate fairly quickly. The female is anxious to find a strong male, with a good territory indicative of his fitness and status, but her pressing schedule allows her very little time to choose. 'She is forced,' writes Dr Clive Catchpole, 'to make a quick decision based only on what evidence the male shows her.' And here is where the male practises his deceit. He will mate with one female in a nest at one end of an extended territory, then move a considerable distance through the reeds to find a new partner. He appears to be an unmated male without wife and offspring to support – and therefore desirable as a father – on a good territory. There is just time for this quick appraisal before the male reed warbler rushes into his usual rapid and aggressive courtship behaviour. The female is quickly swayed and quickly mated.

This deception is allied to strategy number two, based on song. A male normally produces a longer, more elaborate song before pairing than afterwards; a baroque aria to soothe and woo. However, a polygynous male will deliberately emit the longer song even after it has already mated with one female, thus producing, says Dr Catchpole, 'a false cue as to his marital status'. Apparently alone on a territory and producing the special song that signifies availability, the male reed warbler notches up yet another success in his drive to spread his genes among as many females as possible.

Deception and groups

Most forms of deception in nature appear to represent individual attempts to succeed in the normal rough-and-tumble of life – acquiring food, staying out of harm's way and competing for sexual favours. However, there are times when groups of animals will operate a collective conspiracy. Some caterpillars travel together in a coherent line that makes them resemble a snake and thus deters prospective predators. Certain animals that sport startling warning colours will take advantage of the group to heighten their individual impact.

The same principle applies to those animals such as birds or squirrels that get together to 'mob' a likely predator in a show of mock aggression. Here, too, association increases the individual's power to intimidate. The ground squirrels of California live alongside several species of snake which pose a threat to the young squirrels during the time that their mothers are out foraging. In their observations of snake-squirrel interactions, Donald Owings and Richard Coss from the University of California documented instances of groups of squirrels adopting characteristic aggressive poses: erecting the hair, flagging the tail, bobbing the head, pouncing and kicking sand at dangerous rattlesnakes. It is often enough to harass the snake to the point of deterring it altogether.

The chief beneficiary of mobbing should be the mobber. In the case of the Californian ground squirrel, however, the two researchers are inclined to believe that the snake, too, may benefit from the encounter. The mobbing squirrels certainly decrease the likelihood that snakes will enter or remain in their chief area of activity, and therefore they can subsequently afford to be less vigilant – an important advantage because constant vigilance can reduce the amount of time spent on other essential activities such as feeding. On the other hand, suggest Owings and Coss, the repeated feigned attacks by squirrels persuade the snake of the very real threat of injury. Although mobbing is primarily no more than histrionic sabre-rattling, it can nevertheless be stressful to the snake; the more determined the mobbing activity, the sooner the snake learns to slink away. Moreover, since snakes depend on surprise for successful hunting, it would be in their interest to retreat from mobbing, because such conspicuous behaviour only alerts other squirrels to the presence of danger.

Just as a group will try to trick an individual, so too will a single animal sometimes endeavour to deceive a number of others. From his recent observations of flocks of birds in the Amazonian forests, Dr Charles Munn has discovered an interesting new twist to the 'one-tricking-the-many' phenomenon. Among the large, mixed-species flocks of Amazonian birds, there are certain individuals that act as sentinels and give alarm calls if they spot a predatory hawk. When the startled birds take wing, they knock off insects and other tasty morsels from the underside of the foliage. The sentinel birds, flying just beneath the main body of the flock, are able to pick off a beetle or a caterpillar dislodged in this way.

The curious thing, however, is that these sentinels, according to Dr Munn, do not only sound the alarm when hawks fly by. He divided their warning calls into two types: genuine alarms when a hawk was really in the vicinity, and false alarms, indistinguishable from the real, which occurred whenever an insect was knocked out of the foliage. On those occasions there would be competition from the main flock for this food, so the sentinels appear to give diversionary alarms to get their competitors to fly for cover. The alarm-giver, however, does not take cover but simply moves in to take the prey when the coast is clear.

This observation raises a critical issue concerning the use of false alarms. There must be an upper limit or threshold beyond which the sentinel cannot go in raising false calls, otherwise the flock would begin to realize that their lookout was feeding them false intelligence. The sentinel bird wants to avoid the fate of Matilda in Hilaire Belloc's poem who cried 'Fire!' so often that people ended up disbelieving her; or that of the legendary shepherd boy who similarly cried 'Wolf!'

The animals being alerted by the alarm call have to carry out a kind of instinctive cost-benefit analysis. They can hardly ignore a call when the penalty is so great – death in the claws or jaws of a predator. On the other hand, if deception is so commonplace as to be practically the norm, there is a reasonable chance that little harm will come by taking no notice.

In fact, animals that practise deception in this way seem to be able to get away with a relatively high false-alarm rate, estimated at nearly 50% of their total, so great is the potential cost to those ignoring their warnings. Another important point about these tricksters is that they do not mimic the calls of other animals, as is usually the case, but one of their own specialized calls. They have evolved into vocal actors and have mastered the skill of expressing pseudo-emotions in the interests of a full stomach.

Deliberate deception?

If we think back to the stage magician with his bag of tricks, there is clearly one big difference between his kind of deception and that practised by other animals. One is deliberate, the other not. For the purposes of describing the activities of animals, we often use somewhat misleading terms such as 'deceptive strategy' or 'choosing to trick another', as if the creatures concerned have full knowledge of what they are doing. But this is very anthropomorphic, attributing to animals intellectual qualities and intentions that most do not possess. What they do have are deceptive traits, endowed by evolution, which, by working effectively, increase their chances of survival.

Geneticists have calculated, for example, that if an animal is born with even a very slight resemblance to another in its coloration, and if that chance similarity saves the imitator from predation just once out of 10,000 encounters, it will tend to be preserved and elaborated upon in future generations. It is, in short, sufficient of a change to be adaptive.

Note, however, that the animal does not choose to be born with this tiny colour variation, any more than a male garter snake 'chooses' to imitate a female or a hoverfly a wasp. The deception occurs unconsciously, and it occurs because it has evolutionary advantages for the animal concerned. Quite different, then, from the confidence trickster who works out in advance his money-making scheme or the seducer spinning a silver-tongued line to get the girl.

But is deception in animals always of the 'unconscious' variety? Looking at the behaviour of our closest relatives, the primates, we cannot always be so sure. Remember the male langur monkeys we saw in Chapter Six, with bachelors constantly trying to take over the harems of dominants and, if successful, putting to death the young sired by their predecessors. In this way they ensure that females come into heat quickly again ready to father their own offspring. However, langur females sometimes divert the newcomer's thoughts away from infanticide by pretending to be on heat already, even if they are actually pregnant at the time. The new male mates with her and is fooled into thinking that the ensuing baby is his.

Then there are cases recorded in the wild and in captivity of primates using trickery to win or protect food: female baboons that lure a male away from an antelope carcass, chimpanzees that lead companions away from a prized stock of bananas, and so on. In some of these instances it may be, declares Alison Jolly, that primates are displaying behaviour that we associate with humans – foresight, hindsight and the ability to step backwards away from the present and to keep in mind chains of events, particularly what is not true or only may be true. Perhaps the ability of primates to cheat and lie, especially as it relates to an apparent sense of time, shows something like the conscious deception practised by humans.

Self-deception too?

When Ronald Reagan was a candidate running for the US Presidency, he claimed repeatedly that Alaska had more oil than Saudi Arabia. This was factually incorrect. Indeed, it was pointed out to him, proved even, that he was wrong, but still he continued to make the claim. It is a classic example of someone deceiving himself. Self-deception is not confined to politicians. We often lie to ourselves for one reason or another. Imagine, for example, that you find out that a good cause you have been supporting for years is really crooked. You might adopt one of several strategies, either choosing to disbelieve the reports altogether, accepting them completely and voicing your displeasure at the misdemeanours perpetuated, or simply back-

peddling, protesting that you never claimed the organization was all that good, that there were always obvious weaknesses in its administration, and so on. Because it is painful or embarrassing to come clean, you try to rewrite your own little bit of mental history. Think, for example, of how, over the years, your memory of past achievements begins to change. Instead of admitting to being only a moderate performer in the school play, we deceive ourselves into believing that we were only one step down from a megastar stage career.

Tales of power and intrigue. Langur monkeys, Ranthambhor, Rajasthan, India.

Are we the only creatures to deceive ourselves? Probably not, because self-deception could be a useful mechanism for animals in a variety of situations. When we lie knowingly, we may betray tell-tale signs of such deception in our physiological behaviour: shifty eyes, sweaty palms, and a croaky voice may all reveal the stress that accompanies conscious deception. Shown a film of the Russian spy Kim Philby denying his espionage activities, Professor Paul Eckman, an expert in facial expressions and their underlying emotions, can point out tiny cues that give Philby away. However, had Philby genuinely believed he was not a spy, by a process of self-deception, he would have given far fewer revelatory cues. The polygraph or 'lie detector', based as it is on analyzing physiological responses under stress, is far less valuable when used on someone who actually *believes* that what he is saying is true. And one route to self-belief is self-deceipt.

Dr Robert Trivers, thinking about the way animals are constantly evaluating each other in their encounters, suggests that we may not be the only species to practise self-deception. 'Other animals are often in situations of stress in which tight evaluations are being made. Self-confidence is a piece of information that may give useful information about the individual displaying it. If a male is facing off another male in an aggressive encounter, or is courting a female, he may be partly evaluated according to his self-confidence. A certain amount of self-deception in that situation may give a convincing image of his high self-esteem, thereby impressing others.' One is reminded of the championship boxer, keyed up for the big fight, telling himself repeatedly that he can do it, he can win, he has the stamina to go the full fifteen rounds. The net effect is to project an image of supreme self-confidence which can be very intimidating to an opponent. In the fight for survival, other animals, too, may use a similar strategy.

Chapter   Eight

The Next Meal

Every year thousands of tourists visit the famous 'Glow-worm Cave' at Waitomo in New Zealand. They drift silently on boats through the cave, marvelling at the ceiling on which a species of midge called *Arachnocampa luminosa* provides a spectacular bio-light show. The luminous larvae of the fly emit a shimmering glow, designed by evolution not, of course, to impress tourists, but to attract edible insects into their web where sticky threads hold the prey fast. The web then acts as a 'light trap' which can be rapidly switched on and off by the carnivorous larvae as occasion demands. If, for instance, a group of excited tourists begin to talk loudly in their boat, the disturbed larvae will switch off.

The food acquisition strategy of this particular land midge embodies two features that we meet time and time again in the animal world: cunning and communication. There is in-built cunning in these glowing larvae because they combine deadliness with beauty. The mesmeric glow that attracts insects is emitted by a web that may even have tiny droplets of poison on its strands, making sure that the prey remains in the larder for as long as is necessary. There is communication, too, in the cooperative synchrony of the larval light-switching. No use some of the hunters hiding or disclosing their presence if others do the opposite. So when we read the following in Ogden Nash:

> *God in His wisdom*
> *Made the fly*
> *And then forgot*
> *To tell us why...*

we might add a verse of our own:

> *Unless, perhaps,*
> *To illustrate*
> *How the hunted*
> *Meet their fate.*

Hunters human and animal

The 'tally-ho, yoicks' foxhunters in their boots, breeches and 'pinks', blowing horns as they ritualistically follow the dog pack in pursuit of the fear-crazed fox, represent a fancy-dress relic of authentic hunting activity. Indeed, this is hardly 'hunting' at all in the fundamental sense of having to track, trap and kill a prey in order to survive, any more than the bullfight is a match between genuine equals. Nevertheless, hunting, shooting and fishing folk do derive a positive thrill from their sport, removed though it be from its true origins, possibly because these diluted forms of hunting echo a long-standing human necessity, serving as a reminder of a less comfortable past.

Not that humans have altogether ceased to hunt in the ancestral manner. The bushmen of the Kalahari in Botswana use traditional hunting practices that have remained pretty well unchanged for centuries, including implements such as bows and poisoned arrows. Here in the late 20th century we can still see a lifestyle similar to that which some of the earliest ancestors of *Homo sapiens* would have adopted: the fleet-of-foot males going off in a bunch to bring home the food for a number of families.

Among the Kalahari people, hunting is a life-sustaining, practical business, but it is not without its ritualistic elements. Before the hunt, animal bones are thrown in order to judge how auspicious the day is for the enterprise. After the kill, meat is brought back for the women and children, the old and the lame, whereupon a celebratory dance takes place to honour the spirit of the hunted creature. 'We have never killed one of these great animals,' declare the bushmen, 'without saying thanks to it with a dance, for allowing itself to be killed so that we could live. He died that we might live.' It is a truly religious ceremony, filled with magic and mystery, of which we can see graphic prefigurings from thousands of years ago in the quasi-symbolic hunting scenes of cave paintings of other 'primitive' peoples.

Across many centuries and in totally different cultures, hunting people thus share an adherence to ritual; and as we shall see later, other animals, too, may indulge in hunting ceremonies. In the case both of human and animal hunters, an additional essential factor is communication. As the Kalahari bushmen start their hunt, they initiate their cooperative venture with a series of vocal clicks, then whispers, followed by characteristic hand gestures learned from their ancestors. It is a rich unifying language expressly to coordinate their efforts in time and space. Among other hunting animals, cooperation and communication, of one sort or another, are likewise of great importance in achieving their objective: an adequate meal.

Water sport

Cooperation in hunting can assume many forms, varying greatly in style and sophistication. And it can occur in creatures at virtually any level on the phylogenetic scale. The bladder-bearer looks just like an exotic water-lily as it floats under the surface of the water, but in reality it is a beautifully deceptive jellyfish. Its pear-shaped transparent float, pulsating bell-like structures and general appearance of a petal display are all attractive to prey which, when they approach, are stung and devoured. The bladder-bearer, however, is not

Run to ground? The pack investigates a likely bolt hole for the fox, while the 'whipper-in' waits for the rest of the field to arrive.

just one organism but a floating colony composed of several individual animals. This collective hunting party has 'feeding' members which look after the capture and ingestion of prey, and 'reproductive' members that interact with, and are nourished by, the feeders.

Similarly, there is the spectacular sea-comet, a spiral twist of flexible, coloured strands, catching the light as they glisten among the waves and catching, too, the eyes of suitable victims, in this case crustaceans. Again there is division of labour, with stingers and feeders as well as reproducers making up the total organism.

More familiar to human swimmers, for whom they may represent a considerable hazard, is the huge Portuguese man-o'-war, a siphonophore consisting of a bluish float 4 to 12 inches (10 to 30 cm) long, from which hang tentacles that can stretch several yards in length. Attached to the tentacles are numerous polyps primed with stinging cells called nematocysts; in addition to having a defensive function, these can immobilize or kill a suitable prey as the huge tentacles drift over it. This is yet another cooperative hunting organism consisting of a floating colony of individuals.

The notion of an animal being both one organism and a composite of many may seem somewhat strange. Indeed, Professor E. O. Wilson regards the achievement as 'one of the greatest in the history of evolution', because siphonophores have effectively evolved their complex body from 'organs' made out of individual organisms. Other higher animal lines, including our own, evolved organs without passing through this colonial stage. But although

Unchanged for centuries. A Kalahari bushman on the hunt.

127

The expressive pop-eyed squid of the Caribbean, tentacles held up to disguise its shape while it awaits its prey.

the evolutionary pathways may be radically different, the end result is similar.

Communication between the various organ-organisms of the sea-comet or Portuguese man-o'-war is relatively primitive. But there are other tentacled sea-hunters with more complicated predation strategies and languages. Among the various species of squid, these take the form of vivid colour displays combined with distinctive body talk. Squids make profuse and elaborate use of colours. When, in 1903, the German marine biologist Carl Chun hauled on board his cruise boat in the Indian Ocean two small diadem squids, he called them 'jewelled wonder-torches', so taken was he with their ultramarine-blue middle-eye organs, pearly lateral eyes, ruby reds, whites and sky-blues. In fact, squids have various arrangements, depending on species, of luminescent organs or 'photophores', with emissions that change according to circumstance.

While hunting, for example, a squid may vary its appearance from white stripes to yellow flecks or streaks and to complete bars. These shifts in coloration somehow reflect the squid's emotional state, revealing alarm or fear when attacking a larger creature. One function for these displays may well be to lure a prey. Although it is difficult to observe squids in action in their native seas, these relatively poor swimmers do appear to compensate for their lack of mobility by dangling their light-charged tentacles below them. Planktonic organisms, attracted by the light, are caught on the pad of suckers and transferred to the squid's mouth.

Colour can also be used as camouflage, so that the squid can either avoid being hunted itself or remain in ambush waiting for its own prey. Observation and experiment have shown that some species emit different levels of light and a variety of colours at the diverse depths at which they swim, anything from less than a hundred yards to more than five times that depth. The photophores are on their underside, so that these effectively conceal them from animals underneath by harmonizing with the amount of ambient down-welling light at various depths. At the same time, their backs are black and their flanks reflective, so that they are equally well protected on all sides.

Finally, the squid can make use of its expressive body to trick a prey. Just as a professional wrestler will sometimes wave one arm around to distract an opponent from noticing some dirty business with the other arm or the legs, so the squid will attempt to bemuse a prey with its waving tentacular arms. This can have a quasi-hypnotic effect, just long enough for the prey to be duped, poisoned, paralyzed and devoured. Here is deadly body language indeed.

Cooperative hunting: a paradox

In the continual search for victims, some of which are highly mobile and alert, an animal may find it profitable to team up with others of the same species to form a hunting party. The advantages are obvious. The more pairs of eyes there are on the lookout for prey, the more legs to run, wings to flap, or teeth to seize, the greater the likelihood of a successful excursion. What is more, if the prey is eaten in the open, there are that many more eyes and ears alert to the possibility of a predator hunting down the hunters. However, there is one big disadvantage in cooperative hunting; the more individuals there are, the smaller each animal's portion.

Nevertheless, the benefits must presumably outweigh the costs. The hard core of self-interest beneath the apparent cooperation has been demonstrated vividly by Frank Gotmark and his colleagues at the University of Gothenburg, Sweden, in experiments with fish-hunting black-headed gulls. They took small flocks of up to six individual gulls and allowed them to hunt for fish in a swimming pool located in a large barn, timing these fishing sessions

Social feeding among black-headed gulls.

and counting the catch of each bird. They found, on average, that a bird would capture twice as many fish when operating in a flock of six than on its own, even though the fish were, in both cases, always readily available and there were no predators around to distract them. So flocking clearly increased hunting efficiency in some way. The researchers wondered why this should be.

One possible answer is that when the gulls attack a shoal of fish, there is always one gull to lead the way, striking first. This causes the prey to break up into small groups, thereby perhaps making it easier for the following flock of gulls to single out their victims. This, the researchers argued, is all very well for most of the birds, but what about the leading gull? Does it, too, benefit from being the centre of the flock's attention, or is this apparent cooperation really more akin to parasitism? Evidently not. The Swedish scientists were able to measure the hunting success of every individual in the flock and found that even the first gull on the scene is a beneficiary.

Communication is important for the success of the black-headed gull hunting in a flock. The vivid white colours of the bird may make individuals easier to discern, serving as a recruiting signal when prey has been spotted. According to the researchers, 'conspicuous white or contrasting plumage in larids and other seabirds may provide a means, favoured by selection among individuals, of attracting other birds and hence improving hunting success.' Of course, those birds least likely to manage on their own, the weak foragers among the gulls, will benefit especially from the signals given out by other more enterprising members. Hence there is a subtle blend of self- and joint-interest in the predatory activities of the gull. 'Although one might loosely call it "cooperation",' says Dr John Krebs, 'it's really just every individual out for himself and the effect of hunting selfishly in a group is to increase each individual's success.'

Whales and dolphins

A ferociously graphic woodcut print dating from 1590 shows an industrious band of men at Spitzbergen in the Arctic wielding huge knives and axes to dismember a captured whale. In doing so they were continuing a tradition that probably stretched back to palaeolithic times and which was to persist right up to our own era. Whales have always been regarded as a bountiful source of commodities precious to humans. As one Japanese commentator wrote in the 19th century: 'The bones, blubber, meat, intestines and every part of the whale can be made into food.' Since the packages for such nourishment come in wholesale quantities of many tons, small wonder that as maritime technology progressed, so too did whaling, until it reached high industrial levels. As a result, of course, the whale has been over-hunted to the point of absurdity.

In our pursuit not only of food but of other whale-derived substances to fuel our pharmaceutical and, more shamefully, cosmetic industries, we have driven many species to the verge of extinction. Since the turn of the century, for example, it has been estimated that the humpback whale – the singer of extraordinarily beautiful underwater songs – has been reduced in numbers globally by a staggering 95%. Only the efforts of conservation-minded bodies anxious about the potential loss of irreplaceable species, are preventing human hunters from driving the whales forever from the world's oceans. If this happened, we would lose a unique biological resource. The study of whales, as well as dolphins, shows these large-brained mammals to

possess a unique combination of features. Here we may indeed observe, for example, truly cooperative hunting strategies made possible by a high level of 'intelligence' and characterized by the continual use of complex language.

Bubble-nets and sonar detection

Locating and containing the prey is an important aid to the hunter. It is more efficient to work within defined limits than to move around at random hoping for the best. Even baleen whales, which feed by taking huge volumes of water into the mouth, then straining out crustaceans or fish through colander-style baleen plates, has to locate its prey in the first instance. The sea is not uniformly teeming with krill. How the whale knows where prey are likely to be plentiful, from one feeding site to the next many miles away, is still a mystery.

We do know, however, how the humpback manages to take in large mouthfuls of krill in one concentrated gulp. As the whale rises to the surface it exhales a fine column of air bubbles which form an effective net through which fish and krill are reluctant or unable to pass. Reaching the net, the prey turn back, thus constituting a convenient underwater package of edibles for the waiting whale. Professor Don Griffin reflects on the complexity of the humpback's behaviour. 'The coordination of swimming and controlled exhalation necessary for this type of feeding is certainly not a simple reflex action. The whale must first discover where there are enough planktonic animals to make the effort worthwhile, then dive to a suitable depth and

In for the krill: the humpback whale feeding. The intake of food by the whale is enormous. An adult female consumes approximately one ton of fish and krill every day.

Communications technology at sea. Pacific bottlenose dolphins off the Galapagos Islands. Underwater they use echo-location methods for detecting prey.

swim slowly upwards while exhaling bubbles in a coordinated pattern.'

Whales and their close relatives, dolphins, make many audible sounds from boomingly plangent songs to urgent clicks and whistles. They are also sensitive to frequencies beyond those accessible to us, which they seem to deploy for, among other things, the all-important initial location of their prey. The basic technique of these systems is that of sonar echo-location, a method that we have subsequently borrowed for detecting objects under-water. The impetus for our human technology, incidentally, was not predatory but safety consciousness. When in 1912 the famous *Titanic* cruise liner was struck by an iceberg, people began trying to devise ways of detecting large mounds of floating ice in the dark or in dense fog. Then, a few years later, when German submarines started to cripple shipping during World War I, the research intensified.

Under the influence of Sir Hiram Maxim, who was interested in the way that bats – another echo-locating species – can 'see' in the dark, this research lead over the next few decades to the development of echo-locating instruments which would emit sounds at particular frequencies and detect the echoes these made as they bounced off underwater objects, be they enemy ships or, as it was later found, shoals of fish. Thus echo-locating equipment started to be of use in biological research, for tracing the movements of marine animals. And here human technology chanced to converge with that of other species. For millions of years whales and dolphins had been doing something very similar in the pursuit of prey.

A blindfolded performing dolphin can swim easily through an obstacle course or recover objects in a tank. It does so by means of ultrasound. As a hunter in the wild, dolphins appear to use underwater sound emissions in two ways. They have a special ultrasound organ situated just below the blow-hole through which air is forced backwards and forwards in a complex configuration, causing vibrations in the nasal area. A fatty region called the 'melon' focuses these vibrations as a lens brings together rays of light. The intense beam thus produced can be directed by the animal for locating other swimming creatures, including prey, using the echo principle. It may also form a channel of communication between dolphins when separated by considerable distances.

There is even more to the dolphin's ultrasonic apparatus. Whitlow Au and A. E. Murchison, two biologists working in Hawaii, found that when a bottle-nose dolphin located a small sphere underwater, some hundred yards away, it produced an extremely powerful burst of sound in the process. So strong was the emission, in fact, that researchers began to wonder whether the sound beam might act not merely as echo-locator and intercom, but also as a sonic gun to immobilize prey.

Observations of striped dolphins in the wild, preying upon schools of anchovy, reveal that the hunter will circle the school, initially strafing them with sound waves. Then it moves in for the kill, obviously having disorientated the usually regimented fish, which remain as if cemented to the spot, being taken at will by their predator. They literally seem stunned and stupefied by the dolphin's ultrasonic weaponry.

Something similar may be going on among sperm whales. Whales, too, have ultrasonic apparatus in the form of a complicated system of airways in the nasal region. This almost certainly serves as a communication channel for these highly social animals. According to the Russian researchers Belkovitch and Yablakov, this 'ultrasonic projector' may also be able to direct sound of such intensity that it stuns prey such as squid. This helps to explain why the whale, a huge and relatively cumbersome creature, can repeatedly make its daily catch of about one ton of high-speed, jet-propelled squid travelling at anything up to an estimated 20mph (32kph).

As well as those sounds specially adapted for locating and stunning prey, whales and dolphins have a varied vocabulary of clicks and whistles that enables them to cooperate in hunting. An echo-based picture of a prey could be a graphic piece of information to a dolphin, giving it not just a general idea that 'something is there', but also perhaps a fairly detailed three-dimensional picture of the target. In turn, it could relay this data to its fellow hunters. A school of killer whales, for example, will talk repeatedly to one another in this way, all the while encircling their victims or driving them into a part of the sea that is enclosed by land on three sides – a classic battlefield tactic. The hunters will even post a sentry at the outlet to mop up any would-be escapers.

Noisy bats and whistling rats

As the whale or dolphin uses sound to 'see' in the murkiness of the ocean, so too does the bat in its dark cave environment. Bats certainly do not use their eyes for locating prey, as the Italian scientist Lazzaro Spallanzani discovered in the 1790s when he blinded some experimental animals, released them, and established several days later from the contents of their stomachs that they had caught just as much prey as their unblinded neighbours. At the time Spallanzani did not know how bats managed this extraordinary feat. In fact, his 'bat problem' was not solved until well into the present century when a Harvard physicist, G. W. Pierce, developed some apparatus for detecting sounds lying outside the frequency range of human hearing. Using this equipment, Don Griffin carried out a classic series of experiments in which he established that the entire orientation of bats depends on echoes of sounds which they emit almost continuously while flying about. Because these sounds have shorter wavelengths and therefore higher frequencies than those to which our ears respond they are – or at least 99.9% of them are – inaudible.

In his wonderfully informative book, published shortly after his discoveries in 1958 and called *Echoes of Bats and Men*, Professor Griffin describes the language of echoes among a number of bat species, which have been copiously studied by researchers ever since. There is the insectivorous horseshoe bat of Europe, Asia, Australia and Africa, so called because of the U-shaped series of folds around the nostrils and mouth that concentrate emitted sound into a narrow beam. Hanging head-downwards, these bats scan through almost a complete 360 degrees as they seek out their nocturnal

Long-eared bat roosting in the roof beams of a house. They use their ears for 'seeing' prey in the dark.

A moth is detected by a bat as the insect flies within the predator's sonic 'beam'. The bat emits 'chirps', each lasting only 2 milliseconds. The wavelength and frequency of these 50 or so waves vary, with no two alike. The tiny moth disrupts the pattern sufficiently for the bat to home in on the echo it receives.

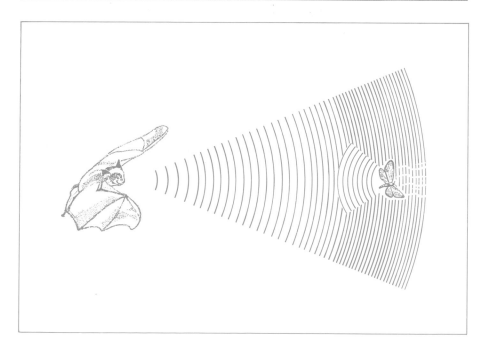

prey. Then there are the highly mobile bats that use their echo-location equipment in flight. Their targets are insects which they hunt by 'tracking their elusive moving prey on the wing, manoeuvring through complicated split-second turns and other acrobatics to follow and intercept the erratic flight of moths and flying beetles, mayflies and mosquitoes'.

If a bat (or for that matter a whale, dolphin or porpoise) is to use echo-location successfully, it needs a fine sense of discrimination to pick out the important echoes indicating a prey from the general mish-mash of sounds that might come back to it, many of them louder than those that mean 'food'. Just as a blind person will learn to discriminate between different treads of footsteps on a staircase, so a bat can selectively distinguish the significant from the irrelevant sounds. In fact, the blind bat and the sightless human both use echo-location for detecting objects or obstacles. Some blind people have trained themselves to respond to the echoes produced by clicking their fingers or whistling, interpreting the input of the reflected sound waves to give them, like the bat, a sound picture of features in their environment.

Once it was established that bats use ultrasonics as a means of gleaning information about the world around them, researchers immediately turned to the possibility that other species might do the same. Certain moths, for example, that might be the prey of a bat, have evolved ultrasonic sensitivities, enabling them to change their flight paths if they detect the high-frequency beams from a bat predator. More positively, it has been found that some moths will ruin a bat's ultrasonic messages by the process familiar to radio operators as 'jamming' – offering their own distorting ultrasonic signals in the place of those of their predator.

Among the more recent chapters in the continuing animal ultrasound story is the work of Dr Julia Chase of Barnard College, Columbia University. Since the 1950s some scientists had thought that rats as well as bats might have a sound-based location system, for these animals, too, are able to hunt successfully in the dark. Dr Chase plugged up the ears of laboratory animals and found, sure enough, they were inefficient at getting around. However, if some form of sonic guidance system were operating, it was unclear at first what they were listening to. She thought that rats were probably using the same kind of high-pitched frequencies as bats, but eventually discovered that this was not the case. Rats, unlike bats, use sounds that are perfectly audible to humans. It takes the form of a little sniff-whistle – a characteristic sniffing noise in which is embedded a whistle at a frequency of 8 kilohertz.

Further research by Dr Chase revealed that the rat does, in fact, have a double sonar system based on two levels of output. 'It's rather like car headlights,' she says: 'they have a low beam for detecting things right in front of them, and that's the sniff-whistle. If they're detecting objects a few yards away they move to a much louder "tooth chatter" sound.' There is also an element of self-preservation in this double level of sound. It would obviously not be sensible for a rat to use sounds that might give away its presence to a predator while it was itself on the hunt. So, says Julia Chase, it probably resorts to the louder tooth-chatter only when really necessary.

A further refinement is that the 8-khz sniff-whistle appears to be a blind spot in the hearing frequencies of hawks and owls, the rat's predators. So there is a sophisticated sound-based hunting strategy in operation here, while the rat itself is not easily detectable by a possible predator. This accomplishment is no mere sideline to the other senses, but an important part of the ancestral sensory repertoire of small mammals. It may extend, too, from rats to mice and hamsters, which may also utilize vision and sound to complement each other in the perennial struggle to eat without being eaten.

The body electric

Nature's hunters are not only radio operators and echo-locators, but also electricians. Such predators operate either in salt or fresh water. Quite a number of fish species have evolved the unlikely adaptation of sensitivity to electric currents, again to detect prey, communicate and, in the case of the Amazonian electric eels or the African electric catfish, cripple their victims.

This sensitivity takes several forms. In some species such as sharks and catfish, electro-reception is employed 'passively', that is for detecting prey and perhaps for direction-finding purposes, exploiting naturally occurring bio-electric or geophysical fields. If a prey moves through the Earth's magnetic field it will, being a conductor, set up what is called a 'motional electric field' that may be detected by a suitably equipped predator. Or if a prey such as a flatfish itself generates a tiny electric charge, this minute voltage gradient could also be detectable.

Studies of the so-called ampullary cells of sharks and rays have shown them to be among the most sensitive of all receptor cells. These astounding cells have such low thresholds for detecting electricity in the water that they can pick up traces equivalent to the field produced by a 1.5-volt torch battery connected to large electrodes that are separated by thousands of miles of water!

Other fish are more active in their use of electricity for hunting. Apart from the strongly electric, aggressive eels and torpedo rays that pack enough charge to stun a human being, there are the 'weakly electric' species which, unlike the powerful individuals that use their knock-out blows only as and when occasion demands, discharge their bio-electricity continuously. The species in question, tropical freshwater fish such as the South American knife fish and the African elephant-nose fish, set up their own instantaneous electric field in the surrounding water from an electric organ situated at their tail end. Any objects, including prey, will distort this field in such a way that the natural generator can detect their presence. The range is quite small, probably not more than 4 inches (10cm), but this is enough to help the fish both to find its way around in its nocturnal habitat and to detect prey in the near vicinity. These electric organ discharges may also be a means of communication, provided two fish are close enough to be within each other's field strengths. Fortunately, the constraints on communication by electricity are not quite so limiting as they are for object detection: the potential range may be as high as 3 yards (2·7 m) under ideal conditions.

Cooperation on the plains

Consider this event witnessed by three ethologists in Amboseli National Park in Kenya: Dorothy Cheney, Robert Seyfarth and Don Griffin. A large herd of wildebeest was grazing in two groups, some near woodland, the others on the open plain, when five lionesses approached. As the wildebeest stopped feeding and watched, two of the lionesses climbed slowly to the summit of two adjacent mounds where they sat down, clearly visible to the whole herd. Meanwhile a third lioness was slinking along the ground to a point midway between the two groups. Suddenly a fourth lioness rushed out of the forest behind those wildebeest grazing near the woodland, chasing the startled

Elephant-nose fish of West Africa, a species with electric organs for prey detection.

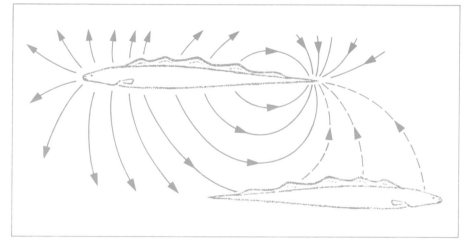

Electric fields radiate outwards and backwards towards the tail of the fish. Distortions produced by a prey within range are immediately detected by the fish's electro-receptors. The exact nature of these distortions depend on the size, conductivity and movement of the prey.

animals towards the other group on the plain. Off they dashed straight towards the place where Griffin and his colleagues had seen the third lioness taking cover. Out she leapt and seized one of the luckless wildebeest, wrestling it to the ground and smothering it with her mouth. Shortly afterwards the other four arrived and ate a leisurely meal.

The whole operation had a calculated precision that made it look very much like intentional and not merely fortuitous cooperation. Don Griffin admits that a single observation cannot be taken as proof of this; but if not, there are a few questions to be explained away. 'Why should two lionesses,' he asks, 'climb to conspicuous positions where the wildebeest could easily see that they presented no serious danger? Why should a third sneak along the ditch to a position about midway between the two groups? Was it pure coincidence that a fourth lioness just happened to rush out from an optimal point at the forest edge to chase the wildebeest over the ditch where one of her companions was waiting?'

It could well be, as Griffin admits, that these lions did not deliberately plot and scheme their hunting tactics. They may have been programmed by natural selection to follow coordinated hunting patterns or they may have just been copying behaviour they had observed in their mothers and sisters.

However, it seems foolish, argues Griffin, to dismiss entirely the possibility that groups of predators such as lions may consciously think about their hunting efforts.

If we do not dismiss the possibility, we have some mind-expanding notions to conjure with: that lions, for example, have a sense of 'future events', because they are plotting something about to happen later on; and that they get round and 'talk' to each other about tactics like generals round a map or football players with their coach. If this is so, how do they communicate? What is the language of lions, with its equivalent of 'verbs' that can presumably express the future tense?

Packs, protocols and pecking orders

Even though they lack the suggested planning capabilities of lions, social predators such as hyenas and hunting dogs benefit greatly from working together in collectives. Single hyenas, for example, rarely succeed in capturing wildebeest calves, but two hyenas together are enough to distract the mother and carry off her young. In fact, many observations of hyenas and hunting dogs preying on Thomson's gazelles and other animals demonstrate conclusively that group hunting is more effective than a solo effort, not necessarily because the predators are collaborating like lions, but probably because they are taking advantage of the greater vulnerability of their prey.

An important determining factor of this success seems to be the discipline of pack animals vis-à-vis their leader. The African hunting dog makes a very good living on the plains, hunting down gazelle, zebra and wildebeest, by following the lead dog in the pack as it relentlessly pursues a target. It is military-style behaviour in which rank structure serves a definite function.

The hunting dog also echoes human activity with its pre-hunt rituals, so reminiscent of the deity-invoking preparations made by the bushmen of the Kalahari or even the Western fox hunter with his warming glass of mulled wine. Packs of hunting dogs go through a curious ceremony just before they move out. The lead dog starts things off with much tail-wagging, muzzling and licking, triggering a raised level of excitement among the rest and, like soldiers synchronizing their watches before a raid, inducing coherence in the group prior to departure. Even after the kill is made, there is more ritual as the young in the pack are allowed to eat first, and the older or lame dogs are fed by the able-bodied hunters.

A cooperative pecking order is also seen among vultures. These, of course, have no need to hunt their prey, being opportunistic feeders on the carcasses left by lions or tigers. But they do not, as one might suppose, simply rip into the carrion without any protocol at all. There is, in fact, an inter-species hierarchy of feeding: the lappet-faced vulture rips open the cadaver for skin and offal; the hooded species digs out soft chunks of meat; and the lammergeier – the only one of the three with head feathers since it does not dip its head into the carcass – devours the leftovers.

Lone rangers

Throughout the animal kingdom, from bird flocks to dog packs, whale schools to insect colonies, some form of social organization, and with it the means of communication that produces collective coherence, occurs repeatedly in hunting behaviour. Indeed for the late W. H. Thorpe, 'Hunting and indeed being hunted provide clear and compelling reasons why natural selection should have favoured some kind of social development.' Sociability,

Social hunting. Hyenas reap the reward of their collective labours.

Ceremonial of the hunt. Wild dogs in the Serengeti National Park, Tanzania, exchange greetings before setting off.

Pecking order: white-backed vultures descend on a carcass already ripped open, while the pink-faced hooded vultures await their turn.

School for carnivores. A lioness, sitting, watches her cubs learning to kill a wildebeest.

however, is obviously not all that natural selection has favoured among hunters, because some, such as the highly successful shark, tend to be loners. So is the lowly and unglamorous earthworm, as it chews its way through soil at one end, excreting most of this at the other, and in between taking from each mouthful what nutrients it needs. But do not be deceived by this apparently random and simplistic hunting system. Not all soils are rich in essential nutrients. The earthworm would be wasting its time if it chewed on regardless of the quality of its intake. Thus even at this level of food gathering there is selectivity, a foraging strategy, if only of a rudimentary kind along the lines of 'change direction if it is not good'.

In other words, the hunter, solo or collective, has to be in tune with its environment. The shark, as we saw earlier, has its electro-reception sense for detecting the tiny muscle potentials produced by likely prey, along with other senses, to help it remain aware of what is happening. Compensation, perhaps, for the many pairs of eyes or ears that would be an assistance for the group hunter. Instead of communicating with others of the same species, therefore, the lone hunter has to commune with its environment, picking up whatever cues it can.

Chapter   Nine

Territorial Imperatives

The language of the estate agent is a veritable code. When a property is described as 'offering considerable potential', the would-be buyer has to substitute the word 'derelict'. Rooms are never 'small' but 'compact', even 'bijou', while a garden not much bigger than a window box attracts the evocative title 'thoughtfully planned'. The euphemisms are based on sound psychological principles, namely that we attach enormous importance to the places in which we live, that this importance is symbolic as much as practical, and that to undervalue or ignore these facts is to strike a personal blow in our direction.

When humans choose a neighbourhood, a road or a dwelling place, they are selecting more than an area in which to live. They are also making a firm personal statement. Their choice of house says something about them just as volubly as their dress or behaviour. There are Apartment Types as there are Little Suburban House with Garage and Garden Types. Inside, there is another batch of classifications to be made according to how the home is designed and furnished: 'Impecunious Liberal'; 'Yuppy Opulent'; 'Downtown Baroque'; the invention is endless.

This deep-seated tendency to adopt highly personal criteria in choosing and furnishing a house is not surprising in our consumer-conscious, affluent society. What is remarkable is how pervasive this need for our own physical and psychological space appears to be even in the poorest, most crowded communities. Even when people are forced by adverse circumstances to live in sparse, cramped conditions they still manage to retain a sense of personal 'territory', respected and avoided by everyone else. Again the technique is to project on to the available space little indicators of one's personal life: the soldier's locker with photographs of family and girlfriend; the prisoner in his cell with his shoebox of prized belongings; the crucifix and icon of the nun or monk. In this way we mark out our territory for our own purposes as much as for the world at large.

Conversely, we become anxious, affronted or irate when what we assume to be our private space is threatened. The intrusion of a neighbour's honeysuckle over our shared garden fence can deeply offend us, while the booming echo of his stereo represents another kind of invasion in the form of unwanted noise. Then, on a grander scale, there is the rush to defend territory in wartime. When the Argentinians occupied the British Falkland Islands – known in Argentina as their Malvinas – the UK Government endeavoured to steer public opinion in favour of armed retaliation. After all, it was argued, this was 'British territory'. What further justification is needed for sending a fleet to teach the transgressors a lesson?

We will therefore fight vigorously to keep the territory that belongs to us, even if this is a long way from the place we recognize as home. Indeed, there is added point in our defence of colonial possessions in that they represent our former expansionist drive to find a wider range of territories in which to settle. They are, like the American West, a tribute to the frontiersman spirit. In the outward drive for territory, there are bound to be conflicts. The West had to be won, not simply taken at will, from an indigenous population doing its utmost to repel the invaders, just as North Americans today are trying to maintain the integrity of their borders against the influx of Mexican 'wetbacks' as the latter attempt to slip illegally across the Rio Grande.

Acquiring, maintaining and defending a territory thus form a basic human need. So too with our animal relatives. We can explain much of what we observe among animals in territorial terms.

Getting there

One of the most spectacular illustrations of home-centred animal behaviour is the uncanny ability of some species to navigate over extremely long distances to a specific point. A Manx shearwater was taken from its nesting burrow off the Welsh coast and flown across the Atlantic by jet to Boston, Mass., where it was released. Twelve days later the bird was safely back in its burrow, having flown some 250 miles (400 km) a day to get there. Similarly, the Laysan albatross returns to its nest on tiny Midway Island in the Pacific, having migrated over distances ranging from 3000 to 4000 miles (4200 to 6500 km).

The reason why these long-haul migrators are able to home so accurately is that they possess a powerful navigational sense or rather range of senses, because not all homing animals use the same techniques. A salmon returning from the middle of the Pacific to its own river is hardly likely to use precisely the same methods as the albatross. As a general rule, however, we can assume that all homing animals must carry the equivalent of a 'map' in their brains, something which tells them that a particular place is indeed home. We now know, too, that they possess in their neural make-up what amounts to a 'compass' to enable them to keep to the right path to reach their desired

End of a long haul. Laysan albatross arrives at Midway Island.

142

objective. The precise nature of those maps and compasses is proving to be one of the most exciting areas of current research.

So far as compasses are concerned, it appears that some animals possess much the same sort of instrument as we ourselves use. Pigeons and bees are both expert navigators, and both have tiny amounts of magnetite in their bodies which respond presumably like the needle of a compass to the Earth's magnetic field. A pigeon can be confused and disorientated by placing on its back a bar magnet producing a stronger and different field from that of the Earth. Interestingly enough, however, this effect is only observed on overcast days; on a sunny day the pigeon gets around quite happily, suggesting that, like all good aircraft, it has another, back-up system for navigation based on the Sun. In fact, the pigeon probably has several other auxiliary compasses as well. It can see in the ultraviolet end of the light spectrum, can respond to polarized light and is extraordinarily sensitive to vibrations. These attributes, combined with the pigeon's wide range of hearing frequencies, may all come into play for homing purposes.

Among fish, the sense of smell seems to be an important navigational aid. It is said that the coast of Australia was smelt by explorers before it was sighted. Likewise, the isolated Spice Islands were given their name by the sailors whose noses detected these aromatic pieces of land before they came into view. Smell is undoubtedly vital for fish making their way with almost magical precision to their breeding territories. Salmon have been shown to be so sensitive to odour that they will be deterred from swimming upstream if a bear should dip its paw in the water, while eels are reputed to be able to detect a pin's head of chemical in more than half a cubic mile of water! An acute sensitivity to smells can provide not only a compass but a map, because an animal can leave its own odour trail to serve as a series of markers for the return journey. Thus, many insects, especially ants, leave scent trails on the outward journey from their nests.

Sight and sound also play a part in animal navigation. The pigeon, attuned to low frequencies, may, in common with other birds, use the 'Doppler effect' (the apparent change in the frequency of sound or light waves, according to the changing distance between the source and the observer) to keep to the right direction, while other animals may simply recognize familiar sound 'landmarks' such as waterfalls, rapids or surf that help them along the way. Like us, animals use their eyes to establish guidance cues. The tiny arctic tern which makes an incredible journey of over 25,000 miles (40,000 km) every year seems to be guided by following familiar coastlines. A human analogue might be the young Australian aborigine who roams farther and farther from home as he goes 'walkabout', all the while noting and remembering significant visual cues for the trip back. Experiments with a number of mammal and bird species have shown not only that they possess good visual recognition apparatus but also, equally important, a fairly long memory for sight cues. One such test with pigeons, for instance, involved training the birds to peck at a particular area in a photograph. It was found that they could do this accurately no less than six years after the original experiment. Just as human navigators have for centuries used stars to steer by, so too do some of our animal relatives. Surely one of the most ingenious animal experiments of all time was carried out to investigate this ability by Dr Franz Sauer, using blackcap warblers as his subjects. In the wild these birds migrate in September by night from northern Germany south-eastwards. When they reach Cyprus they veer due south towards Kenya, thereby missing the hostile Arabian desert. Dr Sauer chose to experiment with blackcap warblers reared from the egg in a planetarium, a place in which he could manipulate at will the birds' celestial environment. He found that it did not matter if the planetarium was wrongly orientated nor if the view of the night sky, as projected on to the dome, was mostly blocked. The birds still began to fly in a south-easterly direction around the time of migration. Then, when the planetarium was adjusted to show the star formations over Cyprus, the fledglings, as in nature, changed course, flying due south. If further manipulations were made to show the Kenyan sky, the pseudo-migration stopped. The birds slept.

From these results, a number of deductions and speculations can be made: that the birds have in their brains the directions in which the stars rise and set, their own directions of movement in relation to the north–south line, perhaps the position of the Pole Star, and so on. This and similar experiments with lesser whitethroats suggest that birds may also remember star patterns for short periods, so that if they are blown off course, their temporary celestial map helps them to find their way back to the desired flight path.

The sailor's feathered friend

The astounding navigational abilities of birds have long been of use to humans. In the biblical story of the Flood, Noah sends out birds when the rains have subsided, in order to look for any uncovered land. It is a myth with many echoes in ancient writings, and understandably so, because birds can sight shore invisible to human eyes. When Polynesian adventurers from Tahiti, voyaging in double canoes, set out to explore the seas 600 years ago, they studied carefully the movements of migrating birds. From their well-defined flight paths, the intrepid sailors could deduce that they were indeed heading for friendly lands, rich in trees and other precious resources, such as the Hawaiian Islands. By observing the flight of the long-tailed cuckoo, Kupe of Raiatea reasoned that to the south-west must be land; following the same course, he discovered New Zealand. Columbus made his first landfall in America by altering course to the south-east when he observed huge flights of land birds heading in that direction, while the discovery of Brazil may also be due to the navigator Pedro Cabral taking advantage of bird flights as natural pilotage. Thus, in our long history of exploration and discovery, we have often been glad to use the in-built skills and navigational instincts of other animals, themselves also a long way from home. Long before we had the technology to construct compasses or print maps, other species, great and small, travelling thousands of miles or even only a few yards, were deploying natural analogues of those invaluable navigational aids. They were also doing something humans always do when they arrive on new soil. They marked it out as their own. For all territories have boundaries; and for animals, as for us, defining those limits is crucially important.

Limiting factors

Like political map-makers, animals will define their territory in an unequivocal manner, using various forms of communication to indicate 'This is mine. Keep off!' With some species it is the sense of smell that picks up the territorial message. A dog alternately sniffing at trees and urinating over them is both establishing its own patch and exploring that of other dogs. We can liken this olfactory language to the shadings in different colours on the political map. Where, on the map, each country and its colonies have their respective colour, so a personal neighbourhood is subtly marked out with 'odour shading'. More obvious is the territorial marker of the river otter which deposits dung and anal secretions to delimit its territory at prominent points along the river bank. By this strategy the otter hopes to put an unequivocal fence around its area that will deter nomadic otters, hunting for a place of their own, from attempting to move in.

A commonly used strategy for maintaining a territory is calling or singing. The male bullfrog is tensely territorial, regularly fighting with neighbours to establish its boundaries. The reason for these frictions is that not all areas are equally desirable. The choicest neighbourhoods, in bullfrog terms, are those parts of the pond least subject to temperature variations which can harm developing embryos, or least likely to harbour leeches that prey on young frogs. The oldest and biggest frogs tend to get the best territories, with the weaker ones settling for something less. Once *in situ*, the males indulge in a lot of calling to reinforce their territorial patterns. After a period of this vocal 'arm-wrestling', the males become familiar with one another's calls; so much so that if a new male happens to arrive on the scene and attempts to take over some territory, the residents immediately recognize a strange call and turn on the intruder. Thus, up to a point, neighbouring frogs are mutually aggressive, but once their fences are up they learn to coexist. From then on, it is the stranger in town that triggers off hostility.

Much the same phenomenon has been observed in birds which proclaim their territory using song. By recording these sounds and playing them back to defined populations of birds, it has been established that birds respond more strongly to the songs of strangers than to the familiar sound of their neighbours. In one such experiment, the male white-throated sparrow's song was played once every 15 seconds during the middle 5 minutes of a 15-minute observation period, and the number of songs of the territory holder was recorded before, during and after playback. The songs played back were varied: the listener would hear a stranger's song, that of a neighbour or its own. The territory holder sang far more in response to a stranger than a neighbour thought to be within its boundaries; and, interestingly, it also sang more in answer to its own song than to a neighbour's.

It is tempting to interpret the host bird's intensified calling in those circumstances as a 'Keep Out' message from territory holder to would-be intruder. However, it was not until 1975 that Oxford biologist Dr John Krebs carried out an important series of experiments actually testing whether this is indeed the intention of the 'defending' bird. Certainly, if territory holders are removed from a breeding population of birds, new birds will immediately fly in from poorer territories nearby to fill their vacated niches. This suggests that, under normal circumstances, something is warning them off, probably the resident male's song.

To make sure that this is so, Dr Krebs conducted a removal experiment with great tits. Territory holders were taken away from their defined patch of woodland and in some territories replaced with surrogates in the form of loudspeakers linked to tape machines that carried their calls. In other territories the tapes were simply recordings of a tune on a penny whistle, while still others were left completely empty. Within a matter of some 8–10 hours, the silent territories were occupied by newcomers, the 'tin whistle'

Tuned in to the territory. A black-capped chicadee can switch songs to make it seem to interlopers that a number of males are in its territory.

areas less so, while the song playback territories were avoided altogether. The conclusion, then, is hard to avoid. When male birds are waiting in the wings ready to take over a territory, they are deterred by the incumbent's song. It represents a kind of vocal show of arms.

This being so, there is obviously much advantage to a bird in being able to sing in such a way as to make the most convincing display, just as humans will parade their most powerful weaponry through city streets to deter the potential aggressor. With birds, complexity of song and variety of repertoire appear to determine the strength of a 'Keep Out' message. Playback experiments show that a territory resounding to a fairly stereotyped, repetitive song is more likely to be occupied than one generating an elaborate, virtuoso call. It could be that the newcomer gets accustomed to a similar call very quickly, while a more changeable sound keeps it guessing for longer.

The fact that a varied repertoire gives a bird a better chance of maintaining its territory opens up some interesting possibilities for deception. The American version of the tit, the chickadee, displays considerable cunning in its singing. Like other birds, it will 'match' the songs of other males, singing a song that resembles another's very closely. In this way it is able to exchange information with other males about the distance between the two birds, because the song will become progressively degraded the farther apart they are. This distance information is an important aspect of maintaining territory. By knowing where others are, male chickadees need waste no time and energy in physically patrolling their patch.

This territorial 'matching' activity is, however, no easy task either for the chickadee or for any other bird that practises it. Each chickadee song is made up of several component 'tunes' which can be switched whenever a rival male chooses. Keeping up with those variations and repeats requires a considerable repertoire on the part of each bird if it is to succeed as a territorial animal. Moreover – and this is where deception comes into the picture – a bird will often generate many different song types in order

Man-made pressures. Cocks fighting in Bali, Indonesia. The two birds are driven to ferocity in the artificial territory of the ring. Their frenzy is matched by that of the wildly bidding spectators.

deliberately to trick rivals into believing that there are a number of males in the territory. Thus a wandering bird, scouting woodland for a suitable area relatively free from competition, will be deceived by one resident into thinking that there are too many others around to make it worthwhile trying to settle.

Further bewilderment comes from the chickadee trick of filling in for a deceased partner. When one of a duetting pair dies, the other will carry on singing both its own and its late partner's song, thus leading others to believe that the territory is still being defended by a pair. Some bird species, such as Cetti's warbler and the North American red-winged blackbird, add another dimension to territorial song deception by constantly moving around the territory, singing at different stages along the way. This again makes the area seem more populous than it really is and has quite a pronounced deterrent effect on intruders; at least, this is the explanation favoured by those who subscribe to the 'Beau Geste Hypothesis'. In P. C. Wren's novel, *Beau Geste*, a legionnaire defending an isolated fort in the desert tricks his enemies into believing that the soldiers are at full strength by propping up dead bodies around the ramparts. It is a classic piece of histrionic cunning. But it was borrowed from the birds.

Stressful territories

On the pleasant island of Jersey in the English Channel is a special kind of territory, or rather group of territories, where animals live in an unusual setting: enjoying the benefits of freedom alongside the security of captivity. The place is the small private zoo founded by Gerald Durrell. What makes this zoo special is that it is predicated on a proper, reasoned concern for its animals' territorial needs. Instead of being confined within an abnormally small or inappropriate space, animals here have enough room to hold an effective territory. Deprived of this amenity, zoo animals will often fight a lot, mutilating themselves and one another, and sometimes die from heart failure. Unlike creatures in the wild, they cannot respond to an unacceptably high population density by emigrating to less stressful domains. The hydra under territorial pressure, for example, produces a bubble beneath its pedal disc and simply floats away. Pharaoh's ants, having removed their brood from their nests, leave for sites deemed suitable by their outrunners, the worker scouts. Mice begin to move around more and explore new territories.

Another artificially created environment that strikes at the territorial needs of animals is the cock-fight, a centuries-old sport still practised in many parts of the world. Game fowl are temperamentally different from normal roosters which usually beat a retreat if placed on another's territory. The game-cock, put on another dominant cockerel's patch, will use its powerful legs and long spurs to fight ferociously, and will try to peck the other into submission. Ironically, this extreme territoriality on the part of the game-cock would not serve it too well in the wild. Too much aggression is frowned upon by the forces of natural selection which tends to favour the evolution of the counterbalancing tendency to run away. In the abnormal circumstances of the cock-fight ring, though, there is no escape route. Driven by the overriding desire to outpeck a rival, fighting cocks show us the dangers of distorted territorial instincts.

Once more, though, we can find natural analogies to this kind of abnormal 'man-made' behaviour under the pressure of increased population density. The hippopotamus is rarely aggressive. It marks its territory, like

Keep off. The bull elephant seal, like the hippo, gapes aggressively when its territory is threatened.

many animals, with bodily excretions, using latrines as signposts, and usually it has plenty of space within these confines to eat and breed. However, under stress the peaceful male hippo becomes a fighter. When the population in the Upper Semliki near Lake Edward reached the alarming density of one animal to only every 5 yards of river bank, males began to attack each other, sometimes fighting to the death. Similarly, the snowy owl usually has a territory of around 12,400 acres (5000 hectares) which it does not feel the need to defend with calls and postures. But there are occasions in the year when the snowy owl is forced by circumstance to cram into an area of little more than 250 acres (100 hectares), whereupon the normally easy-going bird spends much time and effort in making sure that it keeps what little it now has.

An alternative strategy to keeping others out of a territory in order to limit its population density, and hence optimize its resources, is to keep the numbers down *within* the borders. As we saw in Chapter Six, in the experiment with the laboratory mice of Universe 133, there is a natural linkage between breeding behaviour and population size: overcrowding eventually impinges on fertility and mating. In some species the methods of scaling-down are infanticide and cannibalism. Experiments with guppies showed that a single pregnant female in one aquarium will end up as a population of 9 fish, precisely the same number reached by 50 mixed fish in a second tank. The numbers were stabilized at these levels because excess young were consumed by the adult population.

Among social insects such as termites, cannibalism is used as a way of saving food and regulating colony size. Animals are finely tuned to the environment in which they live, recognizing when it is becoming overcrowded and intervening by one means or another to try to maintain the correct balance between territorial resources and population size. One species, however, that seems less expert at these Malthusian manipulations is humankind. We too have circumscribed territories and limited resources, but we treat them as if they were infinitely elastic. In the past there were plenty of natural disasters, plagues and famines to ensure that human numbers did not exceed resources. But today, in many parts of the world at least, this is no longer so. Although the follies of overpopulation are to some extent being regulated by contraception, on the global scale we are steadily becoming like the hippos of the Upper Semliki, filling every inch of available space with bodies while we steadily chew our way through resources that are either non-renewable or not renewable quickly enough. Ultimately, life in the Global Village could end up as a permanent squabble for *Lebensraum* – that all-important living space.

Territories on the move

Animal territories have been compared to an elastic disc, with the resident animal at its centre. The boundaries can be pushed in by growing population density, but when the core territory reaches a certain size, the holder resists and fights fiercely to stop further compression. When pressure eases off, the territorial disc expands, again to a certain limit beyond which an animal is reluctant to try to maintain its supremacy. Although this state of affairs holds true for most animal species, there are some which do not find and try to hold one permanent territorial disc, but are constantly moving around, like nomads on a caravan train constantly seeking pastures new. Sea anemones live in symbiosis with hermit crabs. As the crab moves around, so too does the territory of the anemone. Other species sometimes switch between territorial and non-territorial behaviour according to circumstances. Researchers studying wildfowl on an island off Queensland, Australia, found that these birds adopted the usual territorial pattern during the breeding season, but in winter the flocks were of a hierarchical structure, dominated by the prime or 'alpha' male. The alpha male, along with his harem, ranges over the home territory while other males stay on the periphery of the group, not themselves holding a territory but, like many of the dispossessed, treated as inferior outsiders. Being on the outside can be highly disadvantageous. Those marginal zebras, for example, on the periphery of the herd are the animals most likely to be picked off first by a predatory hyena.

Relatively nomadic species have special problems of communication. A troop of howler monkeys shares about two-thirds of its home range with neighbouring troops, constantly moving around and keeping only a part of the overall territory exclusively for itself at any one time. The howler manages this complicated feat of territorial organization through its distinctive series of calls, each troop identifying its position relative to others and spacing itself out appropriately by exchanging vocalizations throughout the day. If two troops should inadvertently find themselves uncomfortably close when they begin to call, they will indulge in some vocal sparring before going their separate ways. Calling in this manner to maintain mutual avoidance is also common among African mangabeys, with their characteristic 'whoop-gobble' sound.

In their careful respect for others' territorial prerogatives, these monkeys have a lot in common with cats, large and small, which also appear to practise a form of 'time-sharing'. The domestic cat, as well as sharing your fireside,

Call of the nomad.
Howler monkeys in
Venezuela space out
territories by their
vocal exchanges.

also coexists peacefully out of doors with territories occupied by various
other members of its own species. It treads familiar paths from one landmark
to the next, marking out the territorial network with urine. The cat next door
does the same, so that its network overlaps. But both learn each other's
habits so studiously that they never compete for access to their common
areas, except when two males have an interest in the same oestrous female.
Then the time-share arrangement breaks down into sexual squabbling. The
African cheetah also time-shares on a small group basis, with males constantly
scent-marking and examining for traces of other groups, and altering the
direction of their march if the scent is fresh. Should it be more than about
a day old, as judged by the smell-sensitive cheetahs, then the patch can be
encroached upon. Thus cheetah groups peacefully coexist by rarely meeting
each other, while the mutual territory is exploited efficiently to the satisfaction
of all.

Varieties of occupation

The solo domestic cat and the social cheetah illustrate the fact that territories
may be defined and held by a single animal or as a collective enterprise.
With the spotted hyena, hunting in closely knit packs to carry on what William
Thorpe described as 'nature's only organized gang warfare', the communal
territory is marked in a particularly conspicuous way. Indeed it has to be,
for the female-dominated hyena clans can comprise up to 100 individuals,
with a territory as wide as 5·5 square miles (15 sq km). To ensure that other
clans recognize their territory, hyenas will deposit at its core a huge mound
of faeces, which dries and decomposes into a distinctive white column.
This renewable monolith forms a collective deterrent to prospective
trespassers.

In other species, however, the business of marking and, if attacked,
defending a territory falls to individual residents. This becomes an especially
acute problem for animals during mating, when competing males are trying

to assert themselves in order to offer partners evidence of their strength and desirability as fathers. The kob antelope of East Africa adopts a strategy very similar to that of the grouse and other birds by holding special mating areas – leks – to which females in oestrus come for breeding purposes. In each local population of kob, which may be as many as 15,000 animals, there are two kinds of territory, the smaller of which, paradoxically, is the more effective for courtship. The larger patches, of 100–200 yards (90–180 m) in diameter, are called 'single territories', and there is not much competition for them. However, between expanses of these single territories are clusters of much smaller territories, less than 20 yards (18 m) across, which form the true 'territorial ground'. Here males frequently display their strength and dispute with others – in intense competition for what are prime sites. The oestrous female, though courted by males on single territories, hardly ever copulates with them but does so almost exclusively with those holding a

A time-sharing cheetah marks a boundary.

Lekking time for the topi. As with kob antelopes and grouse, the male topi establishes special areas where females come to breed.

small area of territorial ground. She knows that in the hothouse atmosphere of those much disputed little patches, it must be a worthy male that has managed to hold on to his territory.

Just as our house prices go up when property for sale is limited, so too with some animal species territorial behaviour will vary according to circumstances of plenty or scarcity. Thus female marine iguanas in the Galapagos Islands normally are fairly casual about where they lay their eggs, just leaving them in loose soil and departing. On Hood Island there are far fewer sites suitable for egg-layers, so here females compete for space by behaving in ways reminiscent of a typical territorial male, assuming bright colours and fighting. Having won a contest, the triumphant female lays her eggs on a favoured site and thereafter continues to keep an eye on the welfare of her offspring by looking out for predators and sniffing around the site as if to make sure that everything is going according to plan.

Because territories confer so many advantages such as food, shelter, sexual display sites and safe nesting, it is not surprising that they are often the scene of aggressive behaviour, both real and threatened. In the next chapter this is a topic we shall be looking at in more detail. But not all successful territorial occupations depend on a show of might. Nature has generated more subtle means for animals to gain or hold their ground. A case in point is the territorial coral reef fish *Pomacanthus imperator* – the emperor fish – studied by Dr Hans Fricke at the Eilat Nature Reserve in Israel, on the Gulf of Akaba. Males and females of this brightly coloured species share a territory from which they vigorously chase off other adults of the same species, attacking them and escorting them to the territorial border. What interested Dr Fricke is why the defending pair did not seem to resent the intrusion of juvenile emperor fish settling in their territory. Using painted wooden models, one resembling an adult fish, the other a juvenile with its different coloration and patterning, he was able to show that the juvenile 'dress' appears to confer relative immunity from attacks. In fact, juvenile fish are often ignored altogether. According to Dr Fricke, juvenile coloration has evolved precisely to allow the young of a species to cohabit with territorial adults. An altered appearance communicates to adult fish that the creature concerned represents no competitive threat. It says plainly that this is friend not foe.

Landed gentry

While the juvenile emperor fish is born with its age-indicating dress to enable it subsequently to share a territory, in some species of monkey the status of a high-ranking, and therefore territorially powerful animal, may be inherited directly. Like the aristocrat whose land has been handed down through generations from someone who originally had to fight for it, our primate relatives, too, may enjoy the benefits of family connections. According to Dr Alexander Harcourt: 'A number of species of monkey effectively have a system of social class rather like some human societies: dominance status is inherited . . . The offspring of aristocrats become aristocrats, if you like, and proletarian offspring remain among the proletariat.' No need, then, for the fortunate individuals concerned to fight for these privileges; they come, at least eventually, on a familial plate.

Saroj Dalton of Cambridge University discovered that, among rhesus macaques, offspring of high-ranking mothers (not fathers, by the way, perhaps because females mate with a number of males and therefore paternity is

Marine iguana. Hood Island, Galapagos. A female iguana displaying the territorial colours of a male.

Tactile communications: a female vervet monkey grooms a high-ranking female. It is important too for the infant monkey to learn the language of touch.

doubtful) become progressively more dominant as they mature. As one-year-olds they are kept in their place by being defeated by practically all other monkeys in the troop. With age, though, breeding will out, as the high-borns assert their supremacy by dominating the rest and holding the largest territories, much to the chagrin of low-borns who struggle in vain against the system in a series of encounters that Dr Harcourt describes as 'a story of nepotism and power politics that would delight Machiavelli'.

Further observations of other monkey species have shown the story to have all kinds of human-like twists. Among vervets on the Caribbean island of Barbados, Julia Horrocks and Wayne Hunte found that high-borns apparently learn to dominate with their mother's help. Like spoiled aristocratic brats, they pick fights, confident that their powerful mother will support them and ensure that they win the day. 'In other words,' writes Alexander Harcourt, 'in certain monkey societies it is not what you know that matters: it is who you know. It is not how big you are: it is how many high-ranking relatives you have that determines your future status.'

To curry favour with high-ranking females, monkeys will groom them, picking at their fur as a sign of deference, in much the same way as human underlings will fetch and carry for a prestigious individual they wish to impress, making sure, of course, that everyone else notices that they are actually talking to the Great Man. Thus grooming communicates in two directions: to the dominant monkey and to the rest of the troop. As it happens, though, the message comes across only too clearly. The primatologist Robert Seyfarth found that animals grooming with high-ranking females were ousted far more often than those whose attentions were directed at low-ranking monkeys. Cunning can therefore pay off in primate societies, but, like human schemers, primates tread delicately competitive ground, likely to be jostled away from the seat of power by others with the same notion of exploiting good connections.

Although, in their attempts to establish a 'peck order' that accompanies the acquisition and maintenance of a territory, some primates may exhibit a developed social sense, there is still a good deal of struggle and, indeed, aggression involved in achieving their ends. A monkey may claw its way to success by its subtle assessments of which animals are dominant or subordinate, but it may still have to engage in some form of combat to get ahead. Once a territory has been established, whatever the means, monkeys also go to considerable lengths to retain it, deploying, like birds, a wide range of calls designed for that very purpose.

One of the most impressive primate callers is the small, agile gibbon, that astoundingly acrobatic performer in the tropical rain forests of South-east Asia where the dense foliage makes vocal communication a useful means of proclaiming territorial boundaries. The gibbon's call is unusual in several respects. It is, for one thing, compressed in frequency into a narrow band, unlike that of other primates, enabling a sound to travel farther through the thick vegetation than most other primate calls. The calls, too, can be very complex. There is one emitted by the female known as the 'great call', which consists of a long series of unmistakable yodelling whoops coming after a session of male-female duetting that follows a set pattern of exchanges.

According to Warren Brockleman of Mahidol University in Bangkok, these calls may serve a variety of functions, but the most obvious is territorial. The loud vocalizations announce to neighbouring groups of gibbons that here is a pair's territory, thus deterring them from approaching. Then, if an intruder does make its way to the borders, the calls are of sufficient complexity to convey to the interloper the emotional state, physique and social standing of the residents. If vocal language fails, the gibbon, in common with many other animals, has another form of deterrent signal at the ready. Should the intruder come within the territorial boundaries, the defending gibbons will confront it by staring in a characteristic way. Often this facial threat is enough to see off the third party. If not, a fight and a chase will ensue. But such is the communicative power of calls and stares that it is rarely necessary to resort to brute force.

Boundary disputes and the use of threat

Like the gibbon, many species adopt special bodily postures or facial expressions when a trespasser comes on the scene. The black-headed gull draws himself upright in a forced-looking posture like a stern teacher about to reprimand a reluctant pupil, faces his rival or turns to one side and walks parallel to him. Male cichlid fish, in such circumstances, slowly approach each other with their gill-covers raised, while male rats arch their backs and corkscrew around each other with raised fur.

Sometimes these threat displays are made more emphatic by the presence of conspicuous bodily features or organs such as bird crests or ruffs which are raised when a stranger approaches the territorial boundary. With mammals, the ability to erect bodily hair serves a similar threatening function, as does the air-sac on the throat of the tropical frigate-bird which, though normally inconspicuous, is inflated to enormous proportions in threat displays when its bright red coloration becomes a territorial 'stop' light.

Observations of threat displays show them to take place most often at the boundary between territories, which is why, according to Dr Aubrey Manning, these displays are a curiously mixed signal. They take place when the 'tendencies to attack and escape, or, more generally, to approach and to avoid, are both aroused simultaneously and to about equal extents'. The

Thus far and no further.
Mute swans threaten
each other at a
territorial boundary.

whole bodily language of an animal under those circumstances becomes ambivalent. The lesser black-backed gull moves towards a territorial rival with the head raised and the bill pointing downwards; typically signs of the first stages of an attack. But the gull does not attack. Instead it holds back, introducing elements of escape behaviour as the two birds close in on each other, moving the head back, lifting the bill and turning the body sideways and parallel to the opponent. Careful study of these various movements reveals that they subtly reflect slight changes in the birds' underlying attack and escape tendencies. This bodily language is choreographed by the conflicting pressures of standing one's ground and beating a sensible retreat.

Many boundary disputes go no further than such displays. Instead of fighting immediately, a number of species prefer to threaten each other then to withdraw, apparently working on the philosophy: 'Make a big show of strength but if that doesn't impress the adversary, back off!' How often do we see similar strategies being used in human territorial disputes. A neighbour appears to infringe your space, though he regards this as coming fairly within his own boundaries. You shout a lot at each other perhaps, charging the air with threats of lawsuits and retribution. Then, when a deadlock is reached, you cool off and start to come to the inevitable compromise. It happens all the time at the domestic level, as it does in international politics where the big-stick language of threat goes hand-in-hand with the *Realpolitik* of negotiated settlements.

Not that all boundary squabbles stop before the fighting begins. Take

156

the highly organized territorial invasions of 'slave-maker' ants. The slave-makers and the defending ant colonies go through preliminary ritualized displays. But if the slave-makers show superior strength, they will begin to move in. The queen is destroyed – like a radio station being taken by insurgents – and young worker captives taken to become slaves. Some species even use a so-called 'propaganda pheromone' to cause further mayhem. This chemical is secreted by invaders and sprayed on defending ranks of ants, causing them to turn on each other and fight. The maintenance of a territory, however, is not a wholly antisocial piece of behaviour. Just as it is useful in human society to respect boundary limits, so too among birds and other species there is what has been described as the 'Dear-Enemy Phenomenon'. The naturalist James Fisher, writing about his beloved birds, stated: 'The effect is to create "neighbourhoods" of individuals who, while masters on their own definite and limited properties, are bound firmly and *socially* to their next-door neighbours by what in human terms would be described as a dear-enemy or rival-friend situation, but which in bird terms should more safely be described as mutual stimulation.'

Territoriality, then, is not the antithesis of sociality. It is possible, on some occasions at least, to think of one complementing, even reinforcing the other. Animals, like us, do not always need to claw their way to succeed in life. That said, however, in territorial as in many other forms of animal behaviour, violence and aggression are very much in evidence. A mere bunch of red feathers placed in the territory of a robin is enough to trigger off a ferociously persistent attack. Nature, as we shall see in the next chapter, is undoubtedly red in tooth, claw, hoof, fin and feather.

Constructive home-makers

Within its territorial confines an animal will often, though not invariably, make for itself a home. Sometimes this will simply be a matter of selecting a suitably quiet spot, such as a bush or a cave. Often, however, animals will fashion a dwelling for themselves, using locally found materials or even generating components themselves from their own bodies. These building skills are diverse and elaborate, and often involve the use of natural 'tools'. They are also found in all reaches of the phylogenetic scale, among primitive marine organisms, molluscs and crustaceans, nest-building fish, reptiles, rodents, insects, birds and, of course, mammals.

Both males and females can be the home-makers. The norm among fish, such as the intensely territorial stickleback, is for the male to build the nest. The three-spined stickleback digs out a shallow depression and in this excavation constructs a nest consisting of scraps of vegetation which the fish literally glues together with a sticky 'cement' secretion. The layout of the nest shows the stickleback's concern for functional design. It consists of a tunnel lined with plant stems and blades of grass, aligned so that their long axes point along the corridor. With this form of fitted carpet, the stickleback may be creating a series of ventilation spaces below its eggs, so that aerating currents produced by the male's fanning can flow past the eggs on all sides.

Such concern for a proper internal environment is not confined to sticklebacks. Eider ducks and hummingbirds use nest materials as insulators, exercising temperature control over the family home. So too does the sociable weaverbird which builds a spectacular communal nest within a tree canopy. One species found in the Kalahari region of southern Africa has to accommodate an enormous fluctuation in temperature, from blinding desert

The arboreal
architecture of the
social weaverbird.

heat during the day to 14°F (–10°C) at night. Again, choice of material together
with the thickness of nest walls provide 24-hour comfort.

The weaverbird's nest, too, has built-in protection from tropical flooding
in the form of a thick layer of roofing with which the male lines the nest,
before the female weaves a thin inner lining where she will lay her eggs. In
this way there is less chance of chicks becoming drenched by torrential
African rain showers. With other species such as tenebrionid beetles of the
arid coastal region of the Namib desert, the problem is not too much water
but too little. These resourceful water engineers therefore construct shallow
trenches to act as dew-traps, carefully cutting the best profiles to enable them
to extract the maximum amount of moisture.

As well as temperature control and water management, animals also
incorporate ventilation systems within nests or burrows. One species of
worm drives currents of air through the burrow by beating three muscular
organs that act just like extractor fans, eliminating waste and introducing
fresh gases. Caddis fly larvae change the water in the home by undulating
the abdomen.

Domestic security is important in home design. A large proportion of
the 100,000 or so species of ants, bees and wasps, with their advanced social
organization, build complex structures to house and protect themselves. The
construction team is made up of workers which, according to the species,
will burrow into the ground or climb trees to establish a nest. Remarkably,
some workers appear to use inanimate objects as 'tools' in their task. One
such tool-user is a wasp which has been observed holding a piece of stone
or wood in its mandibles, with which it hammers down the soil when finally
closing the nest burrow. Certain ant species secure the nest cavity with leaves
which are pulled together and stuck with silken strands produced by the
larvae. In this case, though, it is the larvae that are the 'tools'. Adult ants hold
them in the jaws, moving them to and fro across the gap in the leaves while
they obligingly extrude their gluey thread.

With the social insects, together with many species of birds and not forgetting the extremely social naked mole rat, we see high levels of cooperation in constructing buildings. Among mole rats there is one work-face animal at the front of the burrowing team, excavating with its teeth the soil which is then passed back down to the tunnel entrance by a conveyer belt of other mole rats lined up behind. There is here organization, discipline and job specialization, just as there is among honeybee workers who can be cell cleaners, cell builders or food foragers. Such coordination implies similarly high levels of communication, probably by pheromones produced both by the queen, to regulate the general nature of the structure, and by individual animals at a more local level to influence the building behaviour of other individuals.

The structures built by animals can themselves be vehicles of communication. The web of a spider is not only designed to trap a prey but also to tell the weaver of the web when a prey has arrived and exactly where it is located. Tiny vibrations are transmitted along the strands to the spider, which is able to interpret these with the skill of an expert signals operator and choose the correct spot to attack. Alternatively, the home itself may be a form of communication. The white booby builds a nest site decorated with thousands of small stones and twigs, yet lays its eggs on the ground. Thus the nest must have some other function. Since pairs of birds are involved in the construction it may be that the purpose is to facilitate the formation of a pair. Working together, they become bonded sexually, the building of the nest serving a ritualist purpose of bringing the partners together. With the bowerbird, as we saw in Chapter Four, the elaborately constructed bower also has a sexual function; serving to enhance the attraction of the male builder in the eyes of a mate and transcending the strictly functional purpose of a place of shelter. Like us, some animals manipulate their living space to make it pleasant as well as practical.

Structural engineering. The nest of the paper wasp of Australia built on repeated hexagonal modules, a design that human engineers often exploit.

Chapter Ten

A Streak of Aggression

Aggression is a multi-coloured creature with many faces. Its habitats are ubiquitous. It feeds on a variety of sources. It can be hostile or it can be welcome. Criminologists worry about the way it seems to be spreading, yet sports coaches actually encourage it in their players. Strange that we should at the same time try to nurture and suppress this familiar member of our society.

In truth, of course, 'aggression' is a very elastic term that covers a multitude of behaviours, both desirable and undesirable, and with all gradations in between. Violent crimes such as rape or homicide certainly qualify as aggressive. Yet so too do the actions of a heavyweight boxer as he pummels the bruised face of a weaker opponent; or those of a tennis player psyching herself up in the final set to give herself that little bit of edge or 'needle' that will carry her aching legs just a shade faster to the volley. And there is the star sales executive who wins his firm's incentive bonuses every month by his driving, get-up-and-go attitude, his fighting spirit in the face of competition. All this we think of as aggressive behaviour. It does not have to involve any direct physical attack on another being. Chess can be aggressive, as can violin playing or even scientific theorizing. Perhaps when you grit your teeth and get down to a hated household chore, that too is 'aggression' – raising yourself to a level of attack for the occasion.

Aggression, then, crops up in many guises. It also holds a peculiarly strong fascination for us. The good citizens of Tokyo, having fought their way home in the evening on sardine-packed underground trains, will then pay to watch enormous Sumo wrestlers, every inch of their colossal bodies trained for aggression, throw themselves at each other in concentrated combat. Meanwhile, on the other side of the world, in Britain or America, the ritualized images of violence in television Westerns or football matches hold millions of people equally enthralled. Even though the newscasts may be filled with horrifying violent stories, still we want more. We will queue to watch aggression and pay good money for the privilege.

In the face of our almost ghoulish need for aggression in our lives, it is tempting to wonder whether we are the only animals to crave such stimulus. We, like the rest of the animal kingdom, have certain basic physical needs which may need to be met by an aggressive streak if we take 'aggression' here in its broadest sense of any behaviour that intimidates or harasses another organism. The hunting animal on the plain chasing down its prey is comparable to our sales representative stalking his monthly targets. But why, given the relative security and ease of modern living, is there apparently so much gratuitous aggression in the human world? More than twenty years ago the ethologist Konrad Lorenz, in his book *On Aggression*, suggested that all aggression is an in-built, inherited tendency which, like any other drive such as the urge to eat or drink, has to find expression. And when it does, the outcome will be violence. This is why, he argues, we use the cathartic effects of sports, prize fights and other contests, to channel away socially unacceptable emotions, just as a lightning conductor discharges unwanted electricity. In short, aggression, according to Lorenz, is inevitable and will out, whatever our upbringing or experience. Others disagree, counter-arguing that our aggression is not necessarily inescapable. We do not need to indulge it in order to survive. The alarmingly big part played by aggressive behaviour in our lives, bigger perhaps than we realize, is by no means fixed and uncontrollable. Perhaps by looking sideways at our animal relatives we can glean a few insights into this fiercely debated issue.

Forms of Aggression

Animals, as we saw in the last chapter, will fight to secure, defend and maintain their living space. They also attack other animals, or at least display aggression towards them, in order to assert dominance. The object here is not so much to shut out others from an area as to prevent subordinates from doing things over which the dominant animal claims priority. In this form of aggressive behaviour, communication becomes extremely important, with

Aggression in the lake. For hippos the prizewinner's purse is access to a female.

Bowing to rank. Aggressive encounters may be prevented among East African hunting dogs if, like wolves, subordinate animals offer the correct appeasement gestures such as mouth licking.

the high-ranking animal signalling to low-rankers its elevated status in a variety of ways. The lemming struts officiously; the rhesus macaque monkey strolls in leisurely fashion with its head and tail raised; the wolf shows its rank with distinctive facial expressions and tail positions. The responses of subordinates are equally characteristic. They show their acceptance of the rank structure by signals of appeasement. A wolf acknowledging another's superiority ritualistically cringes, rolls on its back and exposes its throat before slinking away, tail between its legs. There is no doubt left in the mind of the aggressor that his subordinate is saying: 'Okay, you win.'

Sometimes dominance-induced aggression goes beyond mere gesturing and posturing. As in territorial disputes, what is not settled by a show of force has to be thrashed out in violent confrontation. The normally peaceful male hippopotamus asserts superiority time and time again by symbolic means, urinating and defecating to display its rank, or perhaps indulging in mock fights to keep other bulls in their place, a tack which the subordinates acknowledge by submissive crouching or lip-smacking. More serious encounters, though rare, do take place when a dominant is repeatedly challenged by a male for supremacy. The fight is on. Two colossal beasts, each weighing several tons, tear into each other with their huge teeth for anything up to an hour and a half to establish which of them shall be overlord of that particular territory and have *droit de seigneur* over the females in the harem.

Another form of aggression is sexual. The male hamadryas baboon recruits young females as members of its harem. Once they have become his consorts, the harem-master threatens and harasses them constantly in order to ensure that he retains their favours. Male animals will often threaten or even attack females to get them to mate, even resorting, as we have seen in the case of the mallard duck, to the ultimate act of sexual violence: rape.

In raising their young, parent animals are often aggressive towards their offspring. Like their human counterparts, they need to discipline their charges with mild forms of punishment to keep them close to hand or to urge them along. When the young squabble among themselves, firm intervention by a quick peck or gentle bite has the cold-water effect of a slap on the back of a child's legs. Sometimes parents need to become aggressive when their offspring are making unreasonable demands. Threats and mild attacks are common if the young continue to demand food beyond the age when they should be fending for themselves.

Then, finally, there is 'aggression' in the permanent quest for prey and in attempts to avoid predation. As we saw in Chapter Eight, animals deploy a wide range of wiles, stratagems, techniques and methods to ensure a regular supply of food, all of which operate at the expense of some other species. Conversely, certain prey animals will go beyond evasive or purely defensive action when threatened and launch an attack on their predator. One of the most graphic examples of this is mobbing. A flock of birds mob a potential predator even before the latter has made its move, thereby spiking its guns in a bout of anticipatory violence that can bring serious injury or even death to the more powerful animal.

Harassment and provocation; exploratory aggression

In primates, researchers have noticed another form of aggression which does not seem to fit any of the categories so far described. Young chimpanzees in the Gombe National Park in Tanzania were described thus by Jane Van Lawick-Goodall: 'Infants between 2 and 3½ years of age were often seen pestering older individuals who were peacefully resting or grooming: the infants leaped onto them, biting or pulling their hair, hitting them or dangling above and kicking at them. Such behaviour was invariably tolerated – the adults concerned, either began to play, actively, or merely reached out and pushed the infant to and fro as it dangled.' As with the boxer at the weigh-in or just before the start of the fight, young chimps indulge in a lot of 'pre-aggressive' activity. As well as jumping on adults and pulling their hair, they will throw sand or sticks at them, running away like naughty children if their target jumps to its feet, and coming back soon afterwards to carry on with the teasing. Similar annoying and pestering behaviour is seen in other primate species as well. Langur juveniles harass adults, while young vervets or Java monkeys may pull tails and run off when their teasing gets a response.

Fascinated by what he terms this 'quasi-aggressive behaviour' in primates, Dr Otto Adang of the University of Utrecht in the Netherlands decided to explore it further, with a view to finding out what purpose it might serve. Why do youngsters repeatedly bother to irritate their elders with their playful little mock attacks, even though Dr Adang noted that they were sometimes punished for their misbehaviour? One thought that came to mind was that with chimps, as with humans, the young need to play in order to explore their world. It could be that this teasing of adults served the same sort of function as the playground games of human infants, allowing the young to come to terms with their social environment. To test this idea Dr Adang studied intensively the chimp colony in Arnhem Zoo, consisting of 26 individuals in all, 3 of them adult males, 10 adult females, the rest youngsters.

In all, 184 hours of observation were recorded and carefully analyzed. As a result Dr Adang was able to bear out the 'exploratory aggression' notion because he found that chimp teasing appears to serve several important social functions. It acts to reduce uncertainty in the world of the young chimp. If a youngster's provocations are met by very variable responses on the part of the adult, from the aggressive to the hurt, then the juvenile tends to persist in its teasing. If the adult ignores the child, there are fewer and shorter bouts of pre-aggression. Thus is seems as if the youngster's behaviour is designed to make its social environment more predictable, more certain, more safe.

Another function for aggression is what Dr Adang calls 'investigating authority'. Whereas the uncertainty reduction behaviour is directed at adult females, this type of teasing is aimed at males. Unlike the female adults, males vary little in their reactions, ignoring the taunts most of the time. Here it is as if the young are exploring the limits of authority in the troop, finding out where they stand in the complex social relationships of primate society. Knowing who is boss is an important part of that learning process. The similarities here with the social development of human youngsters are striking. We too acquire our social boundaries and our interpersonal skills by exploratory play. We too 'try it on' with adults and soon learn whether we can push further or need to back off. We too like the world not to be uncertain, to know where we are socially and emotionally, as well as physically. Dr Adang's words, though referring to chimps, are equally valid for us: 'It is just as adaptive for youngsters to explore their social environment as it is for them to explore their physical environment: through exploration youngsters gain vital knowledge for a proper functioning in their surroundings.'

Horses for courses

Many animals have at their command a range of aggressive strategies and methods from which they select the appropriate one for the task in hand. In some deer, antelope or moose species, for example, long, sharp hooves are used as weapons against predators, while horns or antlers are reserved for fights and tests of strength against members of the same species. Even the relatively primitive sea-anemone can display aggressive versatility. For warding off predators the anemone has stinging tentacles designed to deliver a short sharp shock. However, if the beadlet anemone should get into a fight with a neighbour of the same species over territory, those tentacles are withdrawn. Special organs – 'acrophagi' – are produced instead for the battle.

The deadly adder likewise does not use its big guns in the form of its venomous bite when fighting with its own kind. Although competition between males for females is keen (and understandably so since the latter may only be receptive to mating once every two years) male adders prefer pushing and shoving each other to all-out fighting, engaging in a serpentine wrestling match, the celebrated 'Dance of the Adders'. Rattlesnakes, too, display different types of aggression in different circumstances. When males compete for a female, the rattlesnake, like the adder, wrestles in an intertwined test of strength without biting its opponent. On the other hand, when this snake is stalking a prey or lying in ambush, it does indeed strike in all directions and use its bite, without warning the prey with its famous tail rattle. Confronted by an animal large enough to be threatening, the rattlesnake has yet a third aggressive repertoire. Coiling its body, it pulls its head forward to the centre of the coil to assume the striking position and shakes its rattle.

A test of strength. Male Arrowpoison frogs wrestling. Their poison is reserved for predators.

Should the opponent be a king snake, a species that feeds on other snakes, manoeuvre number four comes into play. Now the rattler coils up, hiding its head under its body and slapping at the king snake with a raised coil.

Whatever the particular form of aggressive behaviour an animal adopts, it usually seems only to harm another for good reason: territorial defence, mating competition, food challenges and so on. In fact, it is often said that ours is probably the most aggressive species of all because we will do violence to each other for apparently no reason at all. Our murders, rapes and woundings appear wholly gratuitous in the face of other animals' purposeful aggression. However, is this indeed the case? Are we the only truly violent animals around, killing and maiming to no constructive end? Or can we find similar reprehensible behaviour in other species?

Violent animals

There are two sides to this question, although Konrad Lorenz believed that the issue was pretty well clear-cut when he wrote: 'Though occasionally, in the territorial or rival fights, by some mishap a horn may penetrate an eye or a tooth an artery, we have never found that the aim of aggression was the extermination of fellow members of the species concerned.' Yet when a pack of hyenas has torn apart a wildebeest, they not only squabble and fight for the prey, but they will even try to cannibalize any young that join the noisy feast. Lions, too, will fight each other to the death, while the larvae of insects such as ants and wasp will transform themselves into fighters and eat their fellow larvae in the nest, thereby improving their own chances of survival when food resources are limited. In these cases the animals are powerfully motivated, by hunger or a drive to dominate, to behave aggressively. Yet one could argue that gory fights to the death transcend what is necessary in the circumstances.

Perhaps other animals also enjoy indulging in violence. Perhaps they too may even go about looking for a fight where there is little real cause for conflict. Certainly a cat or a dog will pursue another which it has just put to flight, apparently revelling in its aggression past the point when it needs to display superiority. But would that same cat or dog patrol the neighbourhood looking for another animal to chase? An intriguing experiment with Siamese fighting fish carried out by T. I. Thompson suggests that we are not alone in our gratuitously aggressive appetites. Faced with another male, the fighting fish will raise its gill-covers and extend its fins in a characteristically aggressive display. It will do so, too, when kept in a laboratory tank and the other 'fish' is a mirror image or model projected on to the side of the aquarium. Thompson's fish had a ring suspended in the water. As they swam through it an image of a male appeared, eliciting the usual aggressive behaviour. He found that when the fish were given the opportunity to control their own circumstances, they definitely preferred to swim through the ring. In fact, they did so hundreds of times a day, each time behaving aggressively. Similarly, game-cocks, another species noted for aggressiveness, soon learn in the laboratory to produce the circumstances that will give them the opportunity for aggressive display. Thus it does seem that although there may be nothing concrete to be gained from their behaviour, some species choose to pick fights because they find this intrinsically rewarding. Like any other appetite or even addiction, their aggression can only be satisfied by indulgence.

Aggressive behaviour, especially in the form of a fight, is a very costly

business. It drains an animal of energy. Think of the red deer stag during the rutting season. If approached by a potential rival, it will engage in a fierce display, roaring and slashing at vegetation with its antlers. Should this fail to deter, the contest will take the form of parallel-walking with the two stags advancing and retreating, keeping a respectful distance between them. Next comes a sparring session to test each other's strength. And finally, if the interloper is still not seen off, a full frontal, head-down-and-charge fight will develop. If it does, the costs to the territorial stag can be enormous: a broken leg, antler or lost eye; his harem of hinds dispersed during the clash; severe weakening of a body already fatigued by running the territory. In return for these costs, the stag gains less than one might imagine. Not all the hinds for which he has fought so ferociously, for example, will actually produce calves. Of those that are born, about one in three will die either just after birth or during their first winter. So even with stags and other rutting males such as the ibex, ostensibly directing their aggression to valid territorial and sexual ends, there is a level of violence not wholly matched by the ends they achieve.

In the highly aggressive cichlid fish species *Etroplus maculatus* we find another manifestation of aggression that seems to contradict the idea of animals as being essentially 'non-violent' creatures. It is well known to fish breeders that in order to get a pair of this species to mate and reproduce successfully, they need to put one or two other males in the tank alongside

Aggressive ibex males
clashing on a
mountainside.

the prospective parents. Failing this, the breeding male repeatedly attacks its female, whereas the intrusive males act as whipping boys on which the breeding male can vent its aggression. Now it could well be that this form of violence is territorial and sexual. The presence of the female may arouse territorial instincts in the male, as well as inducing sexual arousal that, as in some humans, becomes directed into a show of physical violence. With other males in the tank these aggressive tendencies can be siphoned off to a third party, a process of 'redirection'. This, according to Professor Aubrey Manning, is familiar behaviour in animals and men when the stimulus that arouses aggression in the first place is for some reason not available for direct attack: 'The boss reprimands his clerk, who in turn cuffs the office boy.'

The urge to kill

If animals, then, do show aggressive behaviours that seem to go beyond the limits suggested for them by Konrad Lorenz, what of human aggression? With the vast catalogue of violent actions accumulated by our species over the centuries – murder, rape, pillage and the mass destruction of modern warfare – are we something special or are we just somewhere on the continuum of aggression, perhaps even only in the middle of the spectrum? According to E. O. Wilson, we should not be too quick to condemn ourselves as the supremely aggressive species. In fact, he goes beyond this to suggest, in opposition to Lorenz, that, far from being exceptionally wicked so far as violence is concerned, we are relatively peace-loving. 'In fact,' he writes, 'if some imaginary Martian zoologist visiting Earth were to observe man as simply one more species over a very long period of time, he might conclude that we are among the more pacific mammals as measured by serious assaults or murders per individual per unit time, even when our episodic wars are averaged in.' Compared, say, to the lions of Serengeti in East Africa, argues Wilson, we are, statistically speaking, less likely to be seen committing serious acts of violence on each other over a given observation period. Even more startling, perhaps, are the observations of Hans Kruuk of a range of flesh-eating animals that show that we, dressed in our hunting attire, are by no means the only species to kill more prey than we strictly need in order to eat. 'Almost all carnivores,' says Kruuk, 'once they find themselves in an enclosure with suitable domestic stock, will kill and kill . . . man is certainly not alone among carnivorous species when he kills without reaping the benefit – we are dealing with a more general phenomenon.'

The notion that gun-toting modern man, obliterating whole populations of animals just for the sake of a photograph, is unique in killing for pleasure has, in Hans Kruuk's view, to be relinquished. Studying bird behaviour in a gull colony in northern England, he found a total of 1449 adult gulls and many more young ones that had been killed by foxes without being eaten. In Serengeti, on one occasion, he found 82 Thomson's gazelle killed and 27 maimed by spotted hyenas, again hardly touched by the predators as food. Such wanton slaughter is by no means rare. Surplus killing is observed among foxes in a henhouse, wolves in a cattle-pen and lions in an ostrich enclosure. Lions are known to kill wildebeest one after another when immigrations of large herds make it especially easy for the predator to ambush its prey. There is also one report of a polar bear slaughtering 21 narwhals trapped by ice. In none of these cases is the need to eat of prime importance.

Why, then, do animals slaughter other species in this wholesale fashion?

The answer, according to Kruuk, lies in the fact that this kind of behaviour occurs when a creature's normal predatory routines do not, for some reason, take place. Usually a hungry animal searches for some time until it contacts a potential prey, then hunts, captures and kills the quarry. If the prey is eaten, the sated predator is disinclined to carry on hunting for more. When a fox breaks into a chicken coop bursting with prey, however, this hunger-search-kill-satiety loop is interfered with. The search and hunt parts of the routine may well be inhibited by the fact that the fox has had a chicken dinner, but the capture and kill components are not. The system that normally works so well in ensuring that the predator wastes no energy on foraging when fully fed and takes advantage of any opportunities for an easy kill that happen to come along, misfires. The food source is wasted because the predator cannot use all the carcasses it has killed.

This is not to say, however, that human aggression of the urge-to-kill variety is both inevitable and excusable. In one important respect we differ from other animals. We have the ability to inhibit natural mechanism by all kinds of moral, cultural and social restraints that we can pass on to others of our species by the processes of communication. The fox has not yet evolved a mechanism for inhibiting its destructive behaviour. 'This may be too much to ask of carnivore evolution,' says Hans Kruuk. 'It should not be too much to ask from Man.'

Aggressive languages

Aggressive behaviour generally plays a constructive and useful role in the world of social animals. It is a means of establishing order in animal societies, enabling groups to live together cohesively. It is also a way of ensuring that only the fittest and strongest males will mate, thereby passing on healthy genes to succeeding generations. In other words, aggression is the everyday mechanism for setting up and maintaining hierarchies of dominance and subordination. However, it has one big drawback if carried to extremes. In offering a challenge or in trying to fend off a competitor, an animal can be injured or even killed if it fights for supremacy. Therefore many species have evolved risk-free confrontational strategies that display aggression without actually using it for real. In these interactions communication is of central importance. Like a military display designed to deter 'The Other Side' or like fractious neighbours shouting elaborate threats to each other in order to impress or intimidate, animals use visual and vocal signals to convey information about their prowess, not all of which is accurate.

This ritualized, gestural aggression takes many forms. Dr Gary Stiles has studied one variant in the Santa Monica Mountains near Los Angeles where Anna's hummingbirds make their habitat. The male Anna's hummingbird is a particularly adept exponent of ritualized aggression. When another bird perches in its territory, the male reacts to this intrusion into his breeding area with a spectacular aerial display of diving. Like an avian Red Arrow, the bird will make a series of dynamic dives, accompanied by calls as it passes by the interloper. This dive-bombing tactic is a show of strength, telling the other male what a fit specimen he is dealing with, and is often used as an alternative to straightforward chasing, depending on how the intruder behaves. Dr Stiles has also found that female hummingbirds, too, will engage in aggressive dive-bombing as they mob an avian predator or another hummingbird close to their nests. The elaborate dive displays appear to vary from one bird population to another, suggesting the possibility, says Dr

Divebomber
extraordinary. The
male Anna's
hummingbird
climbing out of a
successful aerial attack.

Stiles, 'that local "dive dialects" as well as song dialects might develop'.

A number of parrot species also possess complicated repertoires of visual threat displays, especially the small- to medium-sized birds known as lorikeets which inhabit parts of Indonesia, Australasia and the Pacific. Both in the wild and in captivity, lorikeets are exceptionally aggressive towards members of their own and other species, especially in competition for food, perches and nesting sites. Visual signalling plays an important part in these interactions. In his exhaustive studies of lorikeet threat displays, Dr James Serpell of Cambridge University catalogued 19 separate gestures performed by 39 adult parrots, including preening, head-, wing- and body-shaking, scratching, bill-wiping, yawning and stretching, as well as movements such as hopping, flying, leaning and bowing. Each of these characteristic activities signifies a particular kind of threat. What interested Dr Serpell was the relative complexity of gestural sequences put together by individual birds, and the reason why some performed more elaborate rituals than others. He

found that one key feature which tended to influence these displays was bill length. A small-billed lorikeet species can only nick the skin with its bill, while large-billed forms have no trouble in penetrating it and drawing blood. Indeed, a bite from one such species can be powerful enough to splinter wood. Dr Serpell discovered that the longer (and therefore more dangerous) the bill of a lorikeet, the more complex its threat display. The reason for this, he believes, is that a long bill means not only that its possessor can inflict more injury, but that so too can another of the same species. Hence it is mutually beneficial for long-billed species not to fight each other but to signal their aggression in another form. 'As bill-size and the concomitant risks increase,' writes James Serpell, 'selection favours the development of increasingly complex displays as conventional alternatives to physical combat.' What we see in the lorikeet, then, is a kind of graded escalation, with threats becoming more elaborate until a climax point of no return is reached. By introducing a good deal of variety and therefore novelty into its repertoire, the bird is perhaps that much more disconcerting to a rival than if it had a small range of gestures, dazzling an opponent with a kaleidoscopic display ritual that holds the other bird temporarily nonplussed.

From his research on the roaming of the harem-holding red deer, Dr Tim Clutton-Brock finds a similar degree of what he terms 'honest advertisement' among aggressive males. Stags engage in roaring contests on those occasions when a fight seems likely, answering each other's vocalizations with roars of their own delivered at a matching rate to that of the opponent. Challengers seldom press home attacks against stags which have outroared them and rarely win if they do. Again it appears that roaring is linked to the physical prowess of an animal. According to Dr Clutton-Brock, it advertises the bodily condition of a stag which in turn determines the animal's fighting ability during the course of the taxing breeding season or throughout its lifetime. Each stag then makes an assessment of the other's fighting fitness, and therefore its own chances of success, on the strength of the advertisement provided by roaring.

The games animals play

This useful capacity of animals to weigh up the probabilities and possibilities of a future conflict on the basis of information given has been likened to human Games Theory. Just as a poker player assesses the strength of an opponent's hand by the money he lays on the table, or a bidder at an auction computes the seriousness of a rival by his speed and volume of bidding, so too will an animal make a kind of cost-benefit calculation from the signals it receives. Clearly, in such a context, there may be scope for misinformation as well, in the form of bluff. When male monkeys and hippos yawn widely to reveal dangerous canine teeth, their display may not necessarily reflect actual fighting ability, even though it is a pointer to body size. Cats and dogs, faced by an opponent, can raise their fur on end, thereby making their bodies appear slightly larger than they really are. Humans, too, have a small residue of this ability in feeling the prickling of hairs in the nape of the neck. It is a hangover from our ape-like ancestry when the forerunners of humankind had bodily hair that would be erected under threat or stress.

In their pre-fight war-gaming, therefore, animals display honestly and sometimes with a certain amount of bluff – and counter-bluff – in order to give an opponent information that might deter it from attacking. They also display, in response to such advertisement, a good deal of judgment in

A bluffing baboon displays its teeth to deter an aggressor.

assessing their chances, making decisions based on what must be quite fine-grain nuances of visual or auditory signal from the opposing side. We shall be looking a little more closely at the 'mental processes' involved in these games – theoretical assessments – in the next chapter.

Backing off and backing down

Having decided not to press on with its aggressive behaviour, an animal needs to be able to bring matters to a close as unequivocally as possible. There is no point in surrendering unless the opponent recognizes immediately that this is indeed what you are doing. We humans have our 'hands-up' gesture of acquiescence and our white flags of truce. There are equally unambiguous signals among other animals.

African hunting dogs, in common with other canine species, including wolves, indicate their submission by grimacing open-mouthed at their adversary while lowering the head and turning the body stomach-side upwards. In so doing it is clearly offering itself to whatever bites the opponent might inflict. Such abject submission, however, is usually enough to bring any fight to an end. The baboons of the savannahs of South-east Africa have a lifestyle suffused with aggressive behaviour, protecting themselves from outside attacks and maintaining a sexual and social hierarchy within the troop with the oldest, strongest and most experienced males constantly being challenged by young Turks. Again these clashes are preceded by threatening displays – vocal intimidation and stares – which may end in a scrap between animals using long, vicious fangs to try to bite each other. However, it may not come to this if one of the two makes it plain that it wants to back out of the confrontation with a special appeasement gesture. Because dominant ba-

boons will mount subordinates of either sex in a kind of ritualized mating act, this gesture takes the unambiguous form of 'presenting' by the loser to the winner. He displays his rear end in an invitation to be mounted. Immediately his opponent knows that the challenge for supremacy is over. Among other primates submission may be indicated by a cringing scream. Victors, too, may have special forms of acknowledgment of the *status quo*. A victorious monkey may touch or even groom its humbled opponent in an attempt to show that there are no hard feelings and that the two erstwhile fighters can from now on live in harmony.

Without signals such as neck or rear presenting, grovelling bodily postures and vocalizations indicating submission, there would be more risk of animal aggression getting out of control. Mechanisms for defusing potentially explosive confrontations are more necessary in animals that live in close-knit social groupings, otherwise their collective order could rapidly disintegrate. The same is true for humans. We too need to recognize that living together is not a stand-up fight for resources, but a constant give-and-take. Unless we 'get out of control', we try to placate and conciliate when faced with conflict, displaying to the other side by verbal and non-verbal means vital cues that signify a certain amount of compromise on our part. Often, by exchanging such cues, two opponents will keep their difference of opinion on a linguistic level, not resorting to fisticuffs. And they are able to do so without losing face or being humiliated.

Aggression: home and away

Some sports competitions are held on a neutral field in order to eliminate the well-known phenomenon of 'home advantage'. It is of enormous psychological benefit to a team to play at home, in front of friendly supporters. Indeed, many a match between two evenly poised sides has been won on that very basis. Animals, too, compete at home or away in their aggressive encounters, so biologists have begun to wonder whether the choice of territory for the clash could influence the outcome. It looks as if it does. Dr Nicholas Davies discovered that when male speckled wood butterflies get into a dispute over a patch of sunlight on the forest floor, the butterfly already in the patch invariably wins. Furthermore, this outcome could easily be reversed by putting the former loser in the patch for a few seconds. It then wins, displaying a home-field advantage.

Intrigued by this and other similar observations of male red-winged blackbirds, Dr Ken Yasukawa carried out a series of experiments with a bird called the dark-eyed junco to determine whether being on home ground does indeed determine dominance status and, secondly, whether an established home advantage means that a bird needs to be less aggressive in order to win dominance. Sure enough, high-ranking birds which stayed in their home aviary were able to dominate other high-ranking birds which were in an unfamiliar aviary. Where neither bird had a home-field advantage, the two dominance hierarchies mingled. The second part of the experiment, concerning levels of aggression, also produced a positive result. Birds encountering each other on neutral ground fought more than those clashing either home or away. Home-away birds will threaten more but this does not escalate into a fight as often as with neutral-ground birds, because prior residence usually dictates the outcome. 'It seems clear from my experiments,' Dr Yasukawa concludes, 'that the home-field advantage can be an important factor in resolving animal contests.'

Fierce females

As a general rule, across the animal kingdom and including our own species, males are inclined to be more aggressive than females. Just as it is usually men who are convicted of violent crimes, including homicide, and men who organize themselves into hunting or warrior parties, so with other animals it is the male that tends to show aggressive responses. The bull elephant in musth becomes unpredictable and dangerous. The male stickleback, reared in complete isolation from the egg, will set up a territory and vigorously defend it purely under the stimulus that males are driven by the presence of the hormone testosterone in their bodies to become assertive. Higher levels of this substance are found, for example, in those animals that achieve high rank in dominance hierarchy than those at the foot of the dominance scale. In humans, testosterone production can be drastically reduced by removal of the testicles – a fact that has led some American courts to offer a violent offender the opportunity to be castrated as an alternative to a very long stay in prison.

Aggression, nevertheless, is by no means the sole prerogative of males. Females, too, are aggressive, albeit in ways that are less spectacular and therefore likely to be overlooked. Indeed, females also have a certain amount of the 'male' hormone testosterone circulating in their bodies. They, too, like males, tend to organize themselves into dominance hierarchies, using aggression as the means to achieve supremacy. The output of low-ranking females in reproductive terms can fall a long way below that of the dominant creatures, so competition among females for the top spots in the hierarchy, and with them the opportunity to breed, is fierce. Talapoin monkey and Gelada baboon females of a high rank harass their subordinates to such a degree that this causes levels of stress that interfere with their reproductive physiology. The low-status females fail to ovulate and therefore produce fewer children than the dominants. Hence aggression acts here as a competitively inspired contraceptive.

In some species, too, the female can be the bigger and generally more aggressive of the two sexes. This is true for squirrel monkeys as well as for hyenas, where females take a leading role in the clans of hundreds of animals ranging aggressively over large territories. Bird species such as jacanas and phalaropes show almost a complete role-reversal in aggressive behaviour. Here the bigger and more prominently coloured females fight among themselves for control over nests looked after by male birds.

Enhancing aggression

Fighters need weapons. The better these are, the greater the chances of winning. Like us, animals will use their natural weaponry – be this tooth, claw, tusk, hoof or some other, more subtle fighting feature – in offence and defence. Like ourselves, too, they pay a high price for possessing their weaponry. Horns need to be of an appropriate size and shape for their users' methods of attack or defence. Growing horns, however, depletes energy. Moreover, if they are too heavy they may unbalance or slow down their bearer. So evolution does not simply go on generating ever larger horns, teeth or claws, but calls a halt when these reach an optimum size in cost-benefit terms for the aggressive behaviour of the animals concerned. Now that the enormous nuclear stockpiles of the superpowers give both sides the ability to inflict comprehensive 'overkill', it is a pity that humans, too, have not recognized the optimum levels of armament required for the

174

The fruits of aggression. Female talapoin monkey and infant. Less assertive females have fewer children.

job in hand, and stopped there. Like the horns of the reedbuck or ibex, high-technology weapon systems represent a drain on resources that ceases to be productive beyond a certain level.

Not that we are the only animals to use various forms of technology to enhance our aggressive behaviour. Other species, too, have evolved strategies that go beyond the realms of sharp teeth and strong muscles when faced with an adversary. As with the animal architects and navigators we saw in Chapter Nine, the range of techniques is impressive, and many foreshadow technologies that we, millions of years later, have 'invented' for similar ends.

Social insects use pheromones, for example, to act as alarm or warning signals to one another. Like air-raid sirens screaming out the approach of enemy planes, these chemical communication networks incite others to take defensive and sometimes counter-offensive action. The alarm pheromone secreted by bees and wasps is often generated at the same time as poisons or other unpleasant fluids. Thus if a bee becomes roused to sound an alarm pheromonally, it will also discharge substances that will carry the attack back to the aggressor. The coordination of this counter-attack in the form of a beautifully organized swarm is made possible, too, by pheromonal means. So among social insects under pressure of aggression, we see not just alarm systems but battlefield communication links being deployed, using naturally secreted chemicals as the rapid means of passing on military intelligence.

In recent studies of ants and termites, researchers have also been discovering cases where individual insects behave like 'walking bombs'. Dr W. A. Sands of the Centre for Overseas Pest Research, in England, investigated this phenomenon in worker termites scooped from their tunnels in the dark

One-to-one fighting. With stag beetles (*above*) and rhinos (*right*), aggressive confrontations take place between individuals. It is far removed from the impersonality of human warfare.

Wildebeest locked in head on conflict. However energy-expensive and painful it may be, there are good evolutionary reasons for their aggression.

clay-loam soil of a Kenyan hillside. He observed the mandibles of worker termites lunging and snapping at ants in characteristic fashion, but then noticed that as the termite achieved a grip on an ant, another more subtle offensive weapon came into operation. The abdomen of the termite would suddenly contract convulsively, and a special fold of tissue appeared from which droplets of a clear fluid emerged. Twisting its head so as to force the ant to touch this sticky substance, the termite then proceeded to poison its prey.

An even more sophisticated delivery system for firing substances into another's body has evolved in a parasitic fungus called *Haptoglossa mirabilis*. E. Jan Robb and G. L. Barron, from the University of Guelph in Ontario, Canada, investigated the way in which this fungus infects its host, using what they call 'nature's ballistic missile'. The fungus has a special gun-like cell which it shoots through the host's cuticle, thereby inserting a hypodermic-like structure into the target's body. Through the channel of entry thus created, *Haptoglossa* proceeds to pump spores that will multiply at the expense of the unwilling host. Only a fraction of a second elapses between contact with the host and the release of the infective cells in this unusual Trojan Horse-style attack mechanism, which seems to work as effectively as any missile launched from a man-made silo.

There are many other comparisons to be made between the aggressive technologies of animals and man, but in one important respect there is a crucial difference. With animals, aggressive behaviour is usually a matter of one organism directly attacking another, be this victim or enemy. With us, in the age of push-button technology, aggressiveness can operate at a distance. The bomber pilot, miles above Dresden or Hiroshima, or the head-of-state reaching out from a comfortable armchair for the button that will detonate a nuclear Armageddon, know nothing of the individuals whom their actions will harm. Somehow this aggression-at-a-distance seems all the more reprehensible, distasteful even, than the more personalized encounters that prevail among animals. By interposing all the paraphernalia of modern warfare, computer-assisted strategic planning and the technocracy of experts' weapons systems, we are removing some of the natural restraints on aggression that have guided us (and other animals) for so long. Aggression is, for better or worse, a fact of evolutionary life. All animals exhibit it to some degree, so it is reasonable to suggest that it is adaptive, serving a biological purpose. We interfere with it, then, at our evolutionary peril.

Chapter   Eleven

People and Pets

Oakwood Forensic Center in Lima, Ohio, is a state hospital catering especially for people of a violent, disturbed nature, including those convicted of criminal offences such as rape and murder. Some patients are psychiatrically very sick, schizophrenic perhaps, liable to hear bizarre voices in their head that drive them to raging homicide. Some have had shattering childhood experiences that have left them acutely troubled and given to unpredictable anti-social acts of various kinds. Oakwood is not, one might think, an ideal place in which to observe patients displaying love and affection. Multiple killers who will never leave prison might not seem, on the face of it, to be strong on tender, loving care. Nor indeed would you expect depressed or suicidal residents to have anything much to be cheerful about. Wrong on both scores. Here there is affection and there is hope. And the route to both is Oakwood's substantial collection of pet animals.

Hardened prisoners with long histories of violence live for short periods at Oakwood in the company of 150 small pets ranging from macaws, parrots and mynah birds to gerbils, fish, rabbits, parakeets, canaries, guinea pigs and cockatiels. There are also goats, deer, geese, ducks, peacocks and cats for the inmates to care for under the imaginative 'Pet Therapy Program' set up by a psychiatric social worker, David Lee. His experience is that animals can reach intimate parts of the individual that the conventional psychiatric methods do not. When drugs and talking treatments have failed and ECT (electro-convulsive therapy) has brought no results, regular contact with an animal pet can do wonders in rehabilitation. By fondling cats, feeding birds or stroking guinea pigs, chronic patients acquire new levels of self-esteem in a non-threatening environment. 'A bird,' says Dave Lee, 'is not going to make a judgment. You could be a three-time axe murderer, and all it wants is care.'

Having a pet stimulates these prisoners to generate, perhaps for the first time ever, a responsible, care-giving attitude, allowing them to cope with the grinding routines of institutional life and providing a sense of personal identity alongside much-needed companionship. Once pet therapy schemes are under way, it has been found that patients need only half their original levels of medication to keep them psychologically stable. Erstwhile suicide risks find that they have something precious to live for and hold on to life, perhaps identifying with the pets in their care, because most of the latter, fittingly, are similarly disadvantaged, having been brought here instead of being sent to the vet to be put to sleep. 'One of the closest things a person can have,' says one patient, 'is the animals. It helps you survive the trying times, and creates a gentleness within you. The animal gives you warmth and love by giving you faith and trust.' According to another pioneer of pet-facilitated therapy, Dr Alan Beck, a veterinarian who has worked for many years on the therapeutic aspects of pets alongside the psychiatrist Dr Aaron Katcher, such comments are far from atypical. 'Animals elicit affectionate and nurturing care from those who have the worst histories of violence towards other human beings.'

The versatile pet. An inmate at the Oakwood Forensic Center, Ohio, communes with his 'psychotherapist'.

A therapeutic bond

It is not only within the confines of a tight security institution that pets prove to be therapeutically valuable. There is an extraordinarily dramatic film sequence shot some years ago by a French psychiatrist, Dr A. Conderet, when he was treating a little girl who was both mentally disturbed and apparently unable to speak. When a dove was released into the room, however, the little patient leaped up in wonderment, uttering the first sounds ever to pass her lips. Alienated in her silent and troubled world, she was partially released by the mere presence of a beautiful animal. Autistic children have been made more communicative by coming into contact with dolphins in Florida, making clicking sounds similar to those of the animals and generally showing a degree of interest in them that had hitherto been lacking. Ironically, therefore, a pet can sometimes provide a psycho-therapeutic service that no human can offer, without using words – the stock-in-trade of the psychiatrist – but by exchanging other kinds of information. To touch a pet, to feel its sense of dependence, to marvel at its physical qualities, are all valuable outlets for people under stress, both emotional and physical.

One of the most convincing demonstrations of this lies in the healing role of pets in coronary heart disease and hypertension. Patients who have suffered severe coronary heart episodes have a significantly higher survival rate during the first year after discharge from hospital if they keep a household pet, compared to those who do not. Surprisingly enough, just the ordinary day-to-day business of feeding the cat or stroking the dog can have a direct effect on the course of a deadly disease. The same applies to raised blood pressure. Aaron Katcher and Alan Beck have demonstrated that when people talk to their pets in that calmly affectionate voice that humans seem to reserve especially for animals, blood pressure and other physical signs of stress fall markedly to the sorts of levels achieved by a practitioner of transcendental meditation. Beck's conclusion from this and many other similar research observations is that '. . . to be healthy, it is necessary to make contact with *other* kinds of living things. If human beings are going to reach their full potential for health, they must not limit their companions to their own kind. If people are to come to terms with their own animal nature, they must feel the rest of the living world around them.'

The Delta Society

Convinced of the value of interacting with animals as a source of health, both mental and physical, a group of people decided in 1981 to form the Delta Society. Their aims were to promote further research into the nature of this tight bond between humans and pets, to spread more awareness of its value among health-care and social workers, and generally to educate and inform the world at large on the undoubted benefits of animal companionship. Pet lovers the world over, of course, knew already that keeping fish or raising mice give enormous pleasure, while doctors were acquainted with the life-sustaining advantage to the elderly of having a cat or dog around. Old people have been shown to live longer with a pet, because they have something to care for and because they have a live-in therapist constantly helping to de-stress their lives. What the Delta Society has succeeded in doing, though, is to put such observations and experiences on a more solidly scientific footing. No longer is there any need to rely solely on personal anecdotes about the value of pets. Now there are research results to demonstrate it.

The medicinal Macaw. Caring for this bird helps keep the owner's tendency to stress-related diseases in check.

One intriguing example comes from the University of Pennsylvania where Dr Aaron Katcher and Alan Beck teamed up with Herman Segal of the School of Dental Medicine to study the efficacy of animals in reducing the fears and anxieties associated with a visit to the dentist – a stressful time for many if not most people. Among the methods used to mitigate the dread of dental surgery is hypnosis. A patient is helped to relax under hypnosis as a preliminary to treatment, thus curbing the physiological and psychological reactions associated with a trying experience. Could some kind of pet therapy, the researchers wondered, be equally effective?

Dr Katcher already knew that gazing at fish swimming around in an aquarium can be very calming. Indeed, he had installed an aquarium in his own office, finding it relaxing to watch the movements of the fish during difficult or stress-inducing telephone calls. It works, too, with dental patients. Contemplating an aquarium appears to induce as much relaxation as hypnosis, measured by such key pointers as heart rate, blood pressure and subjects' own assessment of their levels of anxiety. The complex, moving patterns of fish seem to act as powerfully as direct hypnotic suggestion, while having the advantage, say the researchers, of being simpler and more acceptable to the patient. But it is not merely the fact that the fish provide a 'complex visual stimulus'. If they are removed from the tank, still leaving a complicated arrangement of waving plants, rocks and bubbling air, the observer's blood pressure drops less quickly. The living element is essential.

An equally impressive therapeutic use of animals has been demonstrated by Dr Carol Antoinette Peacock, a counsellor who works with adolescent boys aged 12–17 who have severe emotional disturbances that lead them into disorderly conduct. Dr Peacock decided to investigate whether her own pet dog might be of use as a 'co-therapist' in treating these boys while they were living in a detention centre awaiting trial. Dividing the 24 subjects into two groups, she interviewed them all, either with or without her dog in the consulting room, for 45 minutes each. Independent testers then assessed the effect of the animal on the boys' replies and attitudes.

The presence of the dog undoubtedly enhanced the interviewees' feelings of relaxation, made them more ready to talk about themselves in detail, and lowered resistance to Dr Peacock's questioning. In other words, the animal's presence helps adolescent patients to participate cooperatively in the process of psychotherapy. They are more articulate, sociable and forthcoming. Other researchers have found much the same with the other experimental groups of patients undergoing counselling or psychotherapy of one kind or another. The hoped-for bond between doctor and patient is somehow established more quickly and more intimately just through the passive intermediary of a pet animal.

Promoting the partnership

Pet keeping is big business. It is estimated that in America alone there are more than 1.2 trillion pet creatures – primarily dogs and cats, but also birds, horses, small mammals, reptiles and fish – on which their owners spend a colossal $4 billion a year on food, and a further $4 billion on various accessories such as collars, cages and toys. Nevertheless, not everyone who might benefit from regular proximity to an animal has access to one. Various organizations, therefore, have been springing up to promote even wider interaction between animals and humans. In Britain, for example, there is the charity PRO Dogs which runs a scheme known as PAT (PRO Dogs Active

Therapy), whereby dog-owners voluntarily take their animals on regular visits to people and places where they will be welcomed. The elderly, in particular, benefit from such schemes, particularly those forced by disability or institutionalization to abandon the idea themselves of being pet-owners. Bereft of close human relationship, an ageing widow can enjoy the feedback of mutual affection, while a disabled child is given an outlet for his or her developing emotional needs by being able to talk to and touch a responsive animal companion. Animals, be they normal domestic pets or even exotic zoo species, can thus provide us with a unique emotional resource.

Pets as patients

In parallel with the recent movement towards understanding, the effects of pet animals on the humans who are near to them is another equally important trend. We are beginning to use our understanding of animal behaviour, in all its manifestations, in order to help animals themselves in emotional or psychological distress. More and more veterinarians are recognizing that, like doctors treating human patients, they need to think of their charges in holistic terms, taking into account the behaviour of animals that are sick as well as their physical condition.

According to Victoria Voith of the School of Veterinary Medicine at the University of Pennsylvania, there are several reasons why this sort of approach is desirable. One is purely self-protective. When a dog wrinkles its upper lip above a canine tooth, this is a sign that the animal is in an aggressive mood, even though the tail may be wagging. Such behaviour indicates that the dog is experiencing, as humans do, conflicting emotions. It may be a friendly and submissive animal but at the time in some pain. The fact that the tail is wagging does not rule out the possibility that, if approached by a stranger, it will exhibit characteristic aggressive-defensive responses.

Secondly, behaviour that is perfectly normal and typical of a species may, under certain circumstances, lead to a health problem. A horse that is socially attached to other horses may strive to remain within sight of the group, even though this means standing for a long time in drenching cold rain. It will shun a warm stable replete with food for the sake of social satisfaction. Conversely, aggression between dogs, both male and female, is commonplace, and this can lead to injury or death. The vet, argues Victoria Voith, should understand the circumstances that contribute to this type of aggression when undertaking treatment.

Thirdly, the veterinarian is usually the first person pet-owners will consult on all kinds of behavioural matters, from problems of house-training to topics such as why a cat will groom itself when it cannot retrieve a tossed paper ball, or why a dog attempts to bury a bone indoors with imaginary soil. They may also have more serious worries about the behaviour of their pets, because animals, like us, can experience 'psychiatric' distress. More and more vets are beginning to appreciate the need to study 'animal clinical psychology'.

Problem pets, problem children

Alongside his regular work of treating physically sick animals, Dr Roger Mugford specializes in 'pet psychiatry'. After surgery hours he visits the homes of people with problem pets, whether they be dogs that are too savage or too timid, cats that are repeatedly dirty around the house, or birds that get so attached to their owners that they wreck the home when left alone. It is significant that Dr Mugford should choose to observe these behavioural abnormalities in a domestic setting. Like a child psychiatrist treating an unruly or disturbed youngster, he believes that much, if not all, of the trouble can be explained in terms of conditioning and upbringing.

As with children, the behaviour and emotional states of pet animals may closely reflect the treatment they receive from those who take care of them. Many violent and ill-disciplined dogs, for example, like delinquent children, are really demonstrating the lack of leadership in their lives. Compared to canine species in the wild, such as wolves, the world of the domestic dog is unstructured. The wolf society has a strict social order with dominant males and females, and a complex communication system based on sounds, body language and smells to maintain the hierarchy. Although the fireside dog retains many of these communicative skills, it has lost its natural, dominant pack leaders. Ideally, a dog's owner should provide that missing leadership. Without it an animal can be excessively aggressive or pathologically timid, like a child that has never been disciplined or shown clearly what it should or should not do. Thus a dog-owner may complain that his pet will not do as it is told when he himself has been indecisive in giving commands or inconsistent in rewarding the animal when it gets things right.

That there is a close parallel between undesirable pet behaviour and child behaviour is illustrated convincingly by the experience of David Tuber and his colleagues at Ohio State University in the simultaneous 'treatment' of Sandy and Jenny, the former a small terrier, the latter a three-year-old child. The dog started to nip Jenny during play in response to her childish enthusiasm and boisterousness, and after a time began to nip other children too, whereas previously it had always been perfectly innocuous. David Ruber decided to try to change the behaviour of both parties by classical conditioning techniques.

Jenny was shown how to pet an inanimate object very gently, being rewarded with candy whenever she did so correctly. Sandy was independently taught to sit on command for a reward of a slice of hot-dog. When this had been achieved, the two were brought together. Sandy was made to sit while Jenny was invited to approach the dog and pet him gently only once. Both were then immediately given their reward. Progressively, Jenny was encouraged to pet Sandy more and more, until both pet and child were in close proximity for a fair length of time without any nipping taking place. Both had been 'reconditioned' by identical behavioural techniques.

Active helpmates

In addition to training animals as pets or using them as relatively passive therapists, we have in the last fifty years or so come to appreciate that they may take a more active role in human welfare. And here careful upbringing and conditioning is not simply desirable but imperative.

Without being blind oneself, it is impossible to appreciate fully the benefits to the sightless of having a properly trained guide dog. The breeds usually trained for the task, namely labradors, labradors crossed with golden retrievers, golden retrievers and German shepherds, possess abilities that complement perfectly their owner's disability. They have pleasant natures, learn commands well, and are not frightened by crowds or traffic. However, above all this, they have a special kind of aptitude that is rarely found in other dogs. They will always obey commands unless – and this is the critical feature – these are contrary to the welfare of their human dependant.

A working relationship: guide dogs for the blind represent one of the most valuable human/animal partnerships.

In our own image.
Yorkshire terriers after
a visit to the hairdresser.

A good send-off for a
faithful friend. As well
as health farms, there
are also pet cemeteries
offering everything
from sumptuously
lined caskets to
engraved headstones.

Pets for sport and status. Falconry in Saudi Arabia. The bird gives its owner recreational pleasure. But it also enhances his social standing.

millions of unwanted pets turned loose every year. Many are discarded Christmas presents, furry kittens or puppies that start to grow into less amenable or less cuddly adult animals.

Some of these outcasts will revert to the wild state, becoming members of feral street packs, relying on dustbins for their food and worrying little about star ratings! All can become a health hazard as disease carriers. A proportion of these wanderers will be rounded up into dog or cat pounds where they are put to sleep. Then their bodies might be sent to 'rendering plants' to be recycled into low-phosphate detergents or sometimes fertilizer. Surely this is the ultimate insult, that having washed our hands of our pets, we wash our clothes in them or enjoy the scents they unwittingly promote in our rose gardens!

There are, then, contradictions and inconsistencies in our relationships with pet animals. Most people will stroke a neighbour's dog but curse the fact that it leaves on the shoes visible and malodorous evidence of its nightly walk along the pavement. At the same time as we value the companionship of an animal, we often lead lives that are too irregular or busy to allow us to give our pets proper care. For those with a lot of money, there are organizations that purport to help. In Los Angeles, for example, Beverly's Doggerie and Animal Center is the pet equivalent to a health-farm where otherwise-occupied film stars can leave their dogs for exercise on a treadmill instead of risking their paw pads on the hot tar of the sidewalks. Unfortunately, though, excess wealth is more often channelled into quite irrelevant aids to a happy pet life: hotels that offer TV sets and Victorian lamp-posts for visiting dogs; establishments with jacuzzis and saunas for tired canine limbs.

Pets as people

The reason why we treat animals as people in this way is, of course, that for many of us a cherished pet virtually becomes a 'person', a fully paid up member of the household. Some of us even go to the trouble and expense of giving pets ceremonial burials in special cemeteries. And we begin to make these human associations very early in life. The world of the baby and infant is full of soft toys in animal form: teddy bears, Snoopy dolls and cloth rabbits, all of which give the child enormous comfort. He or she talks to them, sleeps with them, cares for them in games of hospitals and nurses, while they, for their part, are always compliant, never answering back. It is as if the stuffed cloth effigies represent a portable piece of their mother, constantly on hand to reassure, befriend and comfort. Thus they enable a child to master strange environments and situations without fear, giving them security in tangible form. For adults a pet can serve similar functions. A dog, too, can be a kind of security blanket, faithful, quiet and ready to hand whatever the situation.

Like the child with a doll, we too can talk to our pets and elicit responses. Indeed, by communicating with animals many people have been able to adapt and relate to society in ways that human contacts alone have failed to provide. Pet people will sometimes make claims for their pets that, to the outsider, seem extravagant. They will affirm that a dog 'understands all we say' or that the hearthrug cat is 'more intelligent than any of us'. Is this just wishful thinking? Or do animals possess intellectual powers and capabilities comparable in kind, if not in power, with those of humans? We have seen throughout this book many examples of animals performing remarkable actions. In the next chapter we shall be considering the difficult and controversial question of what might be going on in their minds.

Chapter   Twelve

The Thought
That Counts

Two sides of the same coin. The first is among the Yanomamo Indians of Amazonian Venezuela where an unforgettable 'animal spirit' ceremony is taking place. Elders of the community, under the influence of powerful consciousness-changing hallucinogenic drugs, are possessed by the spirits of animals. As surrogate jaguars or birds, they crawl, growl and flap their arms, threatening, by their monstrous behaviour, the novices, also heavily drugged, who are taking part in an intense ritual initiation. Through humans, the Yanomamo believe, the active spirits of animals are able to communicate.

Thousands of miles away, the other side of the coin. A group of children sits in front of a television set watching cartoon movies. As the familiar characters of Tom and Jerry or Bugs Bunny flit across the screen, their voices and movements, a distorted version of human models, become a vehicle for all the humour, violence, ingenuity and deception that typify our human world. Here animals are being used to communicate human thoughts and emotions. The common denominator is that, in both cases, we are treating animals as if they were human. For the purposes of a religious ceremony or a cartoon entertainment, we are attributing to other species, be they inhabitants of the spirit world or stylized drawings on the movie screen, special powers, including the ability to speak to us.

It is all very anthropomorphic, treating jaguars as spiritual advisers or mice as plucky little entrepreneurs. Sometimes they even obligingly use our own language, adopt our attitudes and generally seem to behave like one of the family *Homo sapiens*. Yet humankind is often regarded as unique in possessing the power to think, feel and communicate. Indeed, in referring to ourselves as the 'thinking primate', we imply that other primates probably do not think and, just as sweepingly, that even more 'primitive' groups and species of animals most certainly do not possess that special capability. If this is so, how unsound it is, ethologically speaking, to lump together intelligent, articulate humans with other animals. They inhabit quite different mental worlds.

On the other hand, some ethologists believe that the idea of animals sharing some of our higher intellectual skills is perhaps not quite so untenable after all. Maybe animals, or at least some of them, *do* think in the sense that we think: making plans; handling abstract concepts; applying memory in its many manifestations to the task in hand; manipulating symbols in adaptable languages; even perhaps fantasizing and dreaming. To do all this would imply another intriguing quality, that of being conscious of self as we ourselves are self-conscious. Looking at your face in a mirror, you see someone that you recognize quite unequivocally as yourself. Might other animals, too, have a similar self-awareness?

Regal plumage. Extravagant masks and head-dresses hide the identity of the displaying male tribesmen in a fertility dance.

Animal spirit ceremony, Brazil. An Amazonian Indian with feathers and facial display marking of a bird spirit.

much of this communication tells the biologist only that certain types of signal have been exchanged with a certain function in view. A bird shrieks a call of alarm. A youngster cries for food. A mouse secretes a socially cohesive pheromone. These signals do not of themselves reveal what, if anything, might be in the mind of the sender or the receiver; what both might think and feel about a situation.

The reason is that such communication is purely confined to the immediate context in which it takes place. The baby cries to elicit food. An alarm call is given to warn of a stalking predator glimpsed in the undergrowth. Were the signal to indicate an animal's concerns about less parochial preoccupations or convey more subtle kinds of information – a cry for food, say, that specified the precise type of nourishment the baby wants or an alarm signal that appears to relay on a message from one individual to a third party – then the creatures concerned would seem to be using their languages in ways that come closer to human communication. We use words and gestures not merely to talk about the here and now but to describe in detail objects and events – real or imaginary – that may be removed in time and space from the immediate circumstances. We use language as a vehicle for thought.

There is a little evidence, debatable though it is, that some animals, especially primates, cetaceans and even social insects, do something similar. In one of their many studies of the vervet monkeys of Africa, Robert Seyfarth and Dorothy Cheney, joined by Peter Marler, set up a playback experiment which seems to show that the three distinct types of vervet alarm call relate

Guard duty in the Kalahari Desert. Like the vervet monkey, the meerkat, a member of the mongoose family, has a variety of alarm signals.

Is the coast clear of predators? Before moving into the open, the cautious vervet monkey utters a distinctive grunt – the 'M.I.O.' Is it saying what *we* would say in similar circumstances?

to three different predators. If the vervet is played what it takes to be a leopard alarm call, it appropriately climbs into a tree: the eagle call prompts it to dive into thick undergrowth; while a python alarm causes the vervet to stand upright and scan the forest for this particular enemy. The researchers regard this as 'Evidence of Predator Classification and Semantic Communication'. The vervet is categorizing its predators and selecting very appropriate 'meaningful' calls to give warning of them, just as we might choose our words carefully to a waiter in order to differentiate between three variants of cocktail.

When worker weaver ants find an interesting food source they go back to the nest and recruit others to help them gather it. This they do by waggling their food-imbued antennae in front of potential helpmates, reinforcing the message with a series of side-to-side head movements. These same ants also recruit support when attacked by other insects, this time by jerking their bodies backwards and forwards in front of nestmates. Their body language is quite different from that in the food-gathering recruitment procedure, even though the end result of the propagandizing is broadly the same: more bodies working together in the common good. Could such signalling differences be telling recruits something specific about the nature of the job in hand, preparing them for food gathering or fighting?

As with the vervet monkey, there may be semantic features embedded in the weaver ant's bodily gestures. What is more, one worker recruit will

195

often pass on the message to others, again making clear the purpose of the signal. In doing so, the passer-on is exhibiting, then, not just semantic comprehension but also perhaps even a degree of 'consciousness', in being able to relay information about an event or phenomenon that it has not directly experienced.

In the case of both the vervet and the weaver ant, we can only say that their behaviour seems to admit of the possibility that such subtleties may be operating in the communication between members of species other than our own. It does not give us watertight proof. In fact, as another observation of the vervet shows, it probably gives us little more than a tentative suggestion because, whenever we observe communication between other animals, we have to guard very carefully against imposing on their exchanges the 'meanings' we might expect humans to express in identical situations.

Monkeys on the move

This is the opinion reached by the philosopher Professor Daniel Dennett after joining forces with Seyfarth and Cheney in an investigation of the meaning of a particular vervet grunt known as the MIO – short for 'Move Into the Open'. It is given typically when a high-ranking male vervet ventures cautiously from the safety of the bush to the exposed plain, and it is answered usually by an identical grunt from another, normally lower-ranking male. What purpose might this exchange of grunts serve, bearing in mind that the vervet is, in general, a taciturn monkey unlikely to grunt just for the sake of it?

A number of possible 'meanings' came to the researchers' minds. The MIO could mean 'I'm going' and the reply, 'OK. Fine', for example, but that would be saying the obvious, so this interpretation was rejected. It could mean something along the lines of 'Follow me', to elicit a 'Yes, sir' from the subordinate, but that too was discarded because, in the strictly hierarchical world of the vervet, such obedience would be taken for granted. For similar reasons of rank, the dominant monkey is unlikely to be requesting a social inferior's permission to move with a grunt denoting, 'May I go' (Answer: 'You may').

Thus Professor Dennett and his associates thought that the most likely meaning of the grunt might be, 'Is the coast clear for me to move?' from a monkey fearful of being attacked as it left protective cover. When the answer, 'Yes, coast clear, off you go', came back, it would begin to move out. At this point a fascinating thought occurred to the investigators.

Vervet males are competitive, always vying with each other for supremacy. If, with his MIO grunt, the dominant animal were asking another whether the coast were clear, it would be in the interests of the latter to feed false information. By saying 'Yes', a subordinate could easily deliver a rival into the jaws of a predator. In a word, the subordinate could benefit from telling a lie. However, it could only do so if it knew something that the dominant did not – namely that a predator was around. And, as the researchers increasingly realized, this is very difficult to conceive of in the everyday life of the vervet.

The lifestyle of the vervet precludes the possession of secrets. 'The close company that they keep,' says Daniel Dennett, 'virtually prevents the opportunity being created for one monkey to have a secret and know that he has a secret – because of course that's crucial.' Thus he was forced to abandon the idea that the MIO means 'Is the coast clear?' because it could only signify as much 'within an institution of communication which has many other possibilities.' At the end of the day, he warns: 'We have to be very careful about imposing the categories from complex human linguistic interactions on to those creatures that have vocalizations that have functions.' These functions could be far simpler than humans are capable of with their 'devious and complicated speech acts'.

The fact, however, that animals do not appear to say what *we* might say in similar circumstances does not of itself rule out the possibility of animal thinking or of animal consciousness. It may make these qualities more difficult to detect or appreciate, but we are still left with a number of observations demonstrating mental powers very reminiscent of our own.

Feats of memory

Sitting in an examination room and faced with a battery of questions designed to get you to regurgitate the facts you have been striving to assimilate over recent weeks, you bless (or perhaps you curse) your memory. Memory, too, stands you in good stead when you are able to give the police officer a detailed description of the person who snatched your purse. However, these are but two random instances; in fact, memory plays a far bigger role in our lives than we usually appreciate.

It is not just the ability to recall facts, telephone numbers, names of party guests from last year or even farther back. We also store in our brains sounds, smells and tastes, together with an enormous variety of other kinds of data, including, of course, the words that make up the languages we speak, read and write. Indeed, some psychologists believe that the storage capacity of the human brain, with its astronomical number of interconnected nerve cells, is so huge that we remember literally everything that we experience: every sound, every picture, every sensation that impinges on us is duly taken into our cerebral data banks there to be stored, though not necessarily retrieved.

So pervasive is the role of memory in our lives, in fact, that it is difficult to imagine any behaviour that might be called 'intelligent' existing without memory to service it. You must have a stock of easily remembered words in order to speak. You must remember what words you have just uttered in order to form sentences. You must have facts and ideas in store before you can reason or argue. Without memory one is a permanent blank sheet, intellectually speaking, oblivious of the past and therefore unable to adapt properly to the present. Precisely how the many, interlocking forms of memory function is something that psychologists are still trying to unravel. But from what we do know already, we can make some telling comparisons between ourselves and other animals.

Consider, for example, the ability we have to take mental pictures of people and places. Our heads are full of such photographs that we can take out from the neural album for reference whenever we choose. Experiments with bees, carried out by the ever-inventive Dr James Gould, seem to show that they, too, may operate by using photographic search images which, hitherto, had been an ability thought to be limited to vertebrates. Bees store information about food sources which they recall when returning to feed. This memory is expressed in the preferences bees show for flowers with particular shapes or patterns.

Researchers had previously suggested that the basis of the bee's memory is that the insect remembers isolated features of preferred flowers such as spatial frequency and line angles, rather than any overall snapshot picture. By training bees to accept sucrose from boxes painted with a variety of carefully designed shapes, Dr Gould was able to show that this is not so. Although the spatial and lineal properties in two designs might be the same, the picture they offered was not. Nor was the sucrose reward for the foraging honey bee. The insect soon learned to distinguish between the two on the basis, it would appear, of the overall image they presented.

Further evidence of the similarity between the workings of human and animal memory comes from the investigations of Dr Anthony Wright, professor in the Sensory Sciences Center at the University of Texas, Houston. Dr Wright's interest is in the way that memory copes with a series of items, such as, for example, a shopping list. Could there be, he wondered, any comparison between the way a human recalls a string of items to be bought at the supermarket and how Rover remembers where he has buried his assortment of bones in the garden?

To test the idea involved devising memory tasks that are identical for both human and animal, and this is in itself far from easy because, according to Dr Wright, 'humans have a long history of taking tests and game playing, and they develop tricks to improve their performance.' Nevertheless, Dr Wright overcame the hurdles with a test of a particular phenomenon in human memory called 'serial position function'. Given a list of items to remember, humans tend to perform better on the first and last items than they do on those in the middle. He showed a series of four slides, containing kaleidoscopic images, to his human subjects. To his animal subjects, namely pigeons and monkeys of the species *Macaca mulatta*, he displayed a different set of slides, this time a series of travel pictures.

The next stage was to flash up on the screen a single slide and get human and painstakingly trained animal to indicate whether that slide had been part of the series of four already shown. Humans and monkeys gave their answers by moving a lever to left or right, pigeons by pecking at a green or red disc.

According to the usual serial position learning curves that other researchers had found, one would have expected both humans and animals to get more right answers for items one and four than two and three. This they did but, from Dr Wright's results, not quite in the expected pattern. If the subjects were tested immediately after being shown the series, they remembered only the last slide. At longer intervals afterwards they remembered both the first and last – the standard memory pattern. Curiously, though, at still longer intervals they remembered only the *first* slide in the series. In other words, the serial function effect, thought to be consistent over time, is more complicated than expected. Moreover, both human and animal subjects, albeit at different intervals, showed precisely the same sequence of memory changes. Thus Anthony Wright breaks down yet another presumed dichotomy between us and other creatures when he concludes: 'The basic memory processes and the interaction of processes producing the serial-position function seem to be similar for pigeons, monkeys and humans.'

Given the obvious familial proximity between us and the primates, we may be less surprised to find a common memory mechanism in humans and monkeys than we are to learn that the humble pigeon shares with us a well-attested mental process. But we should not be surprised at all. To insult someone by calling them 'bird-brained' looks decidedly inappropriate in the light of further investigations of our feathered experimental friends.

Caged conceptualizers

According to the French philosopher René Descartes – he of the famous 'I think therefore I am' proposition – animals differ fundamentally from humans in being unconscious automata pushed and pulled by environmental cues, like toy trains being shuttled around a track. However complicated an animal's behaviour seems to be, he argued, it can be explained purely in terms of unthinking responses or reflexes to external stimuli.

Certainly animals can be conditioned to do a variety of things in this mechanistic fashion. The Russian scientist Pavlov demonstrated this convincingly with his work on reflex behaviour in dogs, while the guru of behaviourism, B. F. Skinner, showed generations of psychologists how potent a stimulus can be in eliciting a desired response. The well-known 'Skinner Box' experiments, for example, in which typically pigeons (or rats) are taught to give the appropriate response, pecking at a particular disc which results in the bird getting a food reward, were prototypes for thousands of similar experiments purporting to show the essentially thoughtless and mechanical nature of animal behaviour.

Give an animal (including here, perhaps, a human being) a particular stimulus and this will produce a response. Reinforce this response, if it is one you wish to be learned, by some kind of reward, or eliminate undesired responses by some form of punishment, and you can shape an animal's behaviour. Behaviour, all behaviour, can thus be manipulated by circumstance. 'Thinking', whatever that is, need hardly enter into the behaviourist scheme of things. This at least is the Skinerian credo. It has to some extent fallen from favour among psychologists so far as the human animal is concerned. Recent experimental observations of other species undermines it still further.

According to Dr Herbert Terrace, this research, including his own work on memory in pigeons, has for the first time shown that an animal can solve certain types of problem without relying on environmental stimuli. 'In order to do so,' writes Herb Terrace, 'the animal must create its own internal representations of past events and use those representations in formulating a solution to the problem in hand.'

In Dr Terrace's experiments a pigeon was required to peck at four coloured discs – red, blue, green, yellow – in particular sequences in order to get the desired food reward. Once the birds learned to peck in a fixed set of configurations, Dr Terrace rearranged the discs in novel combinations and found that they responded as accurately to these as they did to their training sequences. The inference to be drawn is that the pigeons did not perform the pecking task by memorizing a list of particular configurations of colours.

Elaborations of this basic experiment further revealed that the pigeon can discriminate sequences, responding in the affirmative if colours appear in a particular sequence which they had learned, or in the negative if they do not. Herb Terrace compares this to a child's ability to discriminate one nursery rhyme melody from another. And, like a child, the bird manages to discriminate without relying on cues embedded in the task itself but drawing, when required, on sequences that it has 'kept in mind'.

Experiments carried out by Dr David Olton with rats trained to find food in a wheel-shaped radial maze have suggested similar conclusions. The rat manages to find and eat all the food pellets at the end of each arm of the maze with but a single visit to each arm and without entering the arms in a fixed sequence. On one day it might run the maze in, say, the sequence 4–1–7–3–8–6–2–5. On another, a completely different itinerary will be adopted.

Curiously, the animal seems to be able to remember exactly which arms it has already visited, despite the fact that this may have taken place as long as several hours previously. Even though it is always running the maze by different routes, its recall is superb. Herb Terrace comments: 'The rat must not only orient itself in the maze but it must also *represent* the locations of the alleys it has already entered. Whatever the form of that self-generated representation, it cannot be regarded as a conditioned response to some features of the environment.'

The rat, then, seems to store a representation of the places it has visited to be brought forward for reference in the search for food. Like humans, monkeys, bees and pigeons, the rat is capable of filing and retrieving precise information, in this case about important landmarks, independently of outside cues. It holds in its head what psychologists would describe as a 'cognitive map'.

We can push the comparisons even further. One of the key features of human thought is often said to be our ability to form concepts, which means, in effect, being able to establish a general class of idea from a variety of apparently dissimilar particulars. Thus, as the young child soon learns, dogs, cats and sheep, together with teddy bears and Mickey Mouse, all exemplify the concept 'animal'. Show a group of infants pictures of an ash, elm, oak or yew and they will all conceptualize 'tree'. It now seems that other animals, too, can carry out similar conceptual processes, recognizing a class of objects from a number of exemplars.

Professor Robert Herrnstein and his colleages at Harvard University found to their astonishment that, given appropriate rewards, pigeons trained to look at 35mm slides could be induced to tell the experimenters that they saw trees or people or bodies of water and so on. The pigeons are rewarded every time they peck a disc when a slide contains, say, a tree. Thus the bird is being encouraged to find trees wherever and whenever they occur in a colour slide.

This is not an easy task, says Professor Herrnstein, because the trees in his photographs do not usually conform to the child's clear-cut, picture-book representations of trees, with sharply defined trunks, branches and leaves. The slides will contain bits and pieces of trees at different distances from the camera, some in silhouette, some without any leaves, some not at all green. Nevertheless, pigeons, once trained, become very adept at seeing the general principles involved in the concept 'tree'. 'They won't,' points out Robert Herrnstein, 'make such mistakes as calling a stalk of celery a tree. Or a geranium with flowers on it a tree, any more than we do . . . Once they understand what it is they're being rewarded for they can sort out slides for the presence or absence of such things as trees quite accurately.' Pigeons are well known for their visual acuity. An experiment was carried out by the US Coastguard Service in which pigeons were trained to spot people lost at sea, provided they were wearing the distinctive bright yellow lifejacket. But Herrnstein's results show the pigeon able not just to detect but to classify.

Further observations of the pigeon's conceptualizing ability showed that the bird can recognize people as well. In fact, on tests of recognition of a particular woman photographed by Professor Herrnstein in various settings, indoors and out, over the course of a year or so, the laboratory pigeons performed at least as well as Herrnstein himself, even, he admits, 'maybe a little better'. This skill, moreover, is not limited to objects and creatures with which the pigeon would naturally be familiar. It can conceptualize, too, about fish, cartoon characters and letters of the alphabet.

The parrot also can master the concept of a class of objects, according to Dr Irene Pepperberg of Purdue University in Indiana, especially the African grey species which can exhibit 'a number of mental and rudimentary communicative abilities often thought exclusively to belong to humans and certain non-human primates'.

Now the parrot is often thought of as a mere mimic, capable of saying 'Polly put the kettle on' or 'Give us a kiss' after many hours of patient work on the part of its owner, whose speech the bird reproduces in mindless fashion, straining its very different vocal and neurological apparatus to perform what amounts to no more than an amusing parlour trick. But Alex, Dr Pepperberg's experimental subject, is a different proposition altogether. Obtained from a pet store in Chicago, this African grey was, at the beginning of the experiments, 13 months old with, as Irene Pepperberg charmingly puts it, 'no formal vocal instruction'.

First of all it was taught to discriminate more than 40 everyday objects by means of vocal labels, a sizeable vocabulary by any avian standards. Then the researchers taught Alex to 'understand', in a limited way, abstract class concepts. If shown an object, it can correctly identify it, then successfully assign it to a category of shape or colour. Thus when presented, say, with a green triangle and asked 'What shape?' it will in over 80% of cases answer correctly, as it will for 'What colour?' It can also distinguish between materials, allocating objects correctly to 'wood' or 'rawhide' categories.

Irene Pepperberg does not claim, as a result of these experiments, that Alex has advanced cognitive abilities by being able to acquire categorical concepts. But her work does confuse the tidy ideas of those who cling doggedly to a belief in a rigid hierarchy of intelligence in the animal kingdom. Polly the Parrot may still not be a Plato or an Einstein. But neither is it, as we have always thought, only capable of crude stimulus-response imitation.

Articulate Alex, an African grey parrot with some ability perhaps to form concepts.

An eerie case

We must not confuse animal 'cleverness', in all its many forms, with true intelligence, if by this we mean, at least in part, the ability to form abstract concepts, to plan and to reason, to devise strategies at a distance from the site of action. As we have seen in this book, animals are 'clever' in the sense of being able to perform impressive feats such as navigating accurately over long distances or communicating with each other by means of a surprising variety of techniques, some of which resemble our human technologies. Much of this behaviour, though, can be explained in terms of genetic 'pre-programming'. An animal behaves in the way that it does because it is directed to do so by the inherited mechanisms contained in its genes.

A homing pigeon, then, does not 'think' about navigating in the same way that the mariner does as he consults the stars for bearing points. It comes into the world hard-wired, mentally speaking, to behave in the most advantageous way. It is adapted by the vast time-scales of evolution, prepared by countless trials and errors of its forerunners.

Suppose, however, that someone suddenly changes the rules and places such a creature in circumstances for which it is unprepared by evolution? How does it cope with the unpredictable? During his classic studies of the foraging of bees, the great ethologist Karl von Frisch was training the animals to find an artificial food source, moving the food systematically farther and farther away from the foragers. He discovered, to his surprise, that there came a point at which the bees seemed to realise what the experimenter was up to. They began to anticipate his relocations of the food by actually waiting for the feeder to arrive at the place they presumed he would choose.

For an insect this is, according to James Gould, 'an impressive feat'. The bees seem equipped to cope with novel situations produced by the antics of biological researchers, surely not an eventuality that evolution could have designed the bee to meet because, writes Gould: 'It is not easy to imagine anything in the behaviour of natural flowers for which evolution could conceivably have needed to programme bees to anticipate regular changes in distance.'

It really does look as if the bee, along with the rat, the pigeon and the parrot, may be operating with the aid of internal representations of the outside world. Here it may be forming, like the rat in the radial maze, some kind of cognitive map and with it formulating its behaviour which includes some notion of 'future event'. To respond to a stimulus is one thing. To respond in advance of it being given is quite another.

To many of us it is uncomfortable, even fatuous, to leap from a few experimental observations of creatures very remote from our own species to even a tentative claim for their 'intelligence'. But this is probably muddled thinking on our part. The more we discover about the behaviour of other animals, the more we observe not a difference in kind between our intellectual processes and those of birds, insects and mammals, but of degree.

Without doubt, a bee's behaviour is primarily 'mindless', pre-programmed, and automatic. Ours is not. We pick and choose, reason and debate as a basis for our actions far more than any other species. But our cognitive complexity does not make us unique in all respects. Other species, too, share with us some mental features: in how we store information in memory; recognize classes of objects; represent the external world within the confines of the brain.

Sceptics may be reluctant to admit as much in the case of insects and birds, but they are usually ready to concede at least some common ground with our closest animal relatives, the primates. How extensive, though, is this marginal intellectual territory? What really is the evidence that monkeys and chimps, so close to us in their appearance, operate internally in ways that justify the use of the term 'thinking'?

Of apes and men: the great debate

There are, broadly speaking, two kinds of evidence and both involve communication. One is to study carefully the activities of animals in the wild (and sometimes in the lab) in order to compile a detailed list of the various elements of their inter-animal communication, both vocal and gestural. From this, as we saw earlier with Seyfarth, Cheney and Marler's observations of vervet alarm calls, it may be possible to piece together one monkey's language, with the ultimate aim of comparing this to human speech. Do they both involve handling symbols representing objects and events? Are abstract ideas and concepts transmitted in both languages? Do both, in short, display signs that the speaker is thinking? Using communication in this way as a window on to thought can, as we have seen, furnish us with some provocative and challenging results. But the second kind of evidence is even more

Kanzi, the pygmy chimp, using a lexigram at Yerkes Primate Center, Atlanta, Georgia.

thought-provoking. It involves trying to teach other species to use our language so that they can communicate not with each other but with us.

In the mid 1960s a husband and wife team in the psychology department at the University of Nevada, Allen and Beatrice Gardner, undertook an imaginative experiment that was to have profound repercussions in the ethological world, and beyond. Working with a young chimpanzee – a species known for its sociability and readiness to learn – called Washoe, the Gardners set about teaching their protegée to 'talk'. They constructed a special home for Washoe that allowed her free contact with a number of friendly humans, and painstakingly started to teach her human language. But because chimps do not have the vocal apparatus for producing the full range of human speech, the language they employed was that used by the deaf in the USA, namely American Sign Language – ASL.

Washoe at work

The Gardners instructed Washoe in ASL in a variety of ways, working hard to improve the chimp's 'diction' by exaggerating any signs which she had difficulty in reproducing distinctly. In fact, the process by which Washoe acquired her vocabulary of hand and finger gestures was akin to the experience of a human baby learning to talk. Every time an activity was repeated, so too was the appropriate sign. When a door was opened, the sign for 'door' would be made, and so on with a host of familiar objects and actions.

The Gardners recall that ten months after the experiment began, Washoe came to their house, climbed on to the wash-basin and spontaneously made the ASL sign for 'toothbrush', having recognized that implement in a rack. Washoe also displayed an increasing appetite for words. In the first 7 months of training she picked up just 4 signs; in the next 7 months 9 signs; but in the next period 21 words. What is more, she showed that she could manipulate these with some discrimination. Whenever confronted by any kind of smell, Washoe would at first sign 'flower'; later she acquired separate signs for flower and smell. Finally, and most exciting of all, was the propensity the chimp showed for using her stock of words in combinations, forming little phrases or sentences along the lines of 'open-food-drink' to indicate 'open the refrigerator'. She would thus manage to convey one idea by combining the words for a series of other ideas, rather as the German language puts together composite nouns such as 'Flugzeug' (literally 'flight apparatus') for 'aeroplane' or 'Segelflugzeug' for 'glider' ('sail-flight-apparatus').

To researchers into animal thinking and consciousness, not to mention philosophers, these seemed like quite extraordinary accomplishments. Here was an animal that could, apparently, learn to use human language in much the same creative ways that we use it. When a plastic doll was found stuffed into the chimp's regular cup, Washoe signed ruefully 'baby in my drink'. Surely this was definite evidence of that subtle manipulation of symbols characteristic of human language?

On reflection, however, it seemed to some observers that the evidence offered by the Washoe experiment was not as convincing as at first appeared. Other, similar projects were set up. Dr Herb Terrace undertook to teach language to a chimp initially with a view to challenging the contention of the linguistician Noam Chomsky that the human use of language is unique. Accordingly he trained his animal, 'Nim Chimpsky', to acquire a large stock of words in ASL but was ultimately disappointed by the results. Most of Nim's output was pure repetitive stuff, asking for food and drink and the like, without much evidence of the backward and forward chit-chat of true conversation.

It could have been that, compared to Washoe, Nim was not up to the task in hand. Some have called him Dim Chimpsky. Dr Terrace, however, prefers to consider his efforts as nothing more than complex tricks analogous to a dog scratching the door to indicate that it wants to go for a walk. Chimps, of course, have a much wider repertoire than a dog, but their apparently sophisticated use of signs is in essence identical to that of mindless manipulators such as dogs. A chimp, believes Terrace, will only use a sign to request

Tool using. A chimp uses a stick to pick out termites. This young animal has acquired his skill in manipulating tools by observing and imitating older chimps.

a specific object, as a demand signal. Unlike a child, it will not, without prompting, dispassionately draw your attention to a feature of the environment, such as a passing cat, just for the sake of saying 'I see the cat, you know'.

Lana, Sherman, Austin and Kanzi

At the same time as Herb Terrace was working with an ASL-speaking chimp, other researchers were going in slightly different directions, and some were arriving at very diverse interpretations of their results. ASL, they felt, for various reasons was not the best language to teach an animal. Thus David Premack taught Sarah to handle plastic words, while Dr Duane Rumbaugh and his colleague and wife Sue Savage-Rumbaugh opted for arbitrary patterns that stand for words, called lexigrams, in a series of experiments that were to throw wide open once more the whole question of talking, thinking primates.

The Rumbaughs, working at the Yerkes Regional Primate Research Center, Emory University, undertook a chimp teaching programme based on the specific series of lexigramatic symbols they created, called 'Yerkish'. In this, symbols composed of curved and straight lines arranged in various combinations and depicted on different colour backgrounds, stand for different words. Using it does not require the manual dexterity of ASL, and this makes it suitable, too, for teaching mentally retarded children to communicate. Indeed, this was the origin of Yerkish and the primate communications programme, because by modelling the basic processes of acquiring language in experimental apes, the Yerkes team hoped ultimately to gain insights into the difficulties of youngsters who had been unable so far to learn to talk. Use of the programme was further facilitated by the installation of a specially designed computer keyboard containing the lexigrams.

The first chimp to use the prototype keyboard in 1972 was Lana, who learned to request food with lexigrams and to answer simple questions from her teachers. One day Lana was introduced to a younger chimp called Columbus and the two became quite good friends, with Lana showing considerable care in the way she handled the newcomer. Once the two were left together in Sue Savage-Rumbaugh's room for some time. When she peeped in at them, she found them asleep, their limbs entwined. On the projector above Lana's keyboard were, in lexigram form, the symbols denoting: 'YOU COLUMBUS COLUMBUS'. Left alone, the trained chimp appeared to be trying to communicate with the younger animal by means of the symbolic language of Yerkish.

This in itself was an exciting thought, but the exploits of two more chimps trained by the Rumbaughs were to prove even more intriguing. Sherman and Austin proved to be very adept at learning their lexigrams. They also showed that they could ask for, give and receive food from each other, using only Yerkish as their channel of communication, perhaps 'the first documented instance of symbolic communication between primates'.

Once this kind of interaction had been established, Sue Savage-Rumbaugh decided to test the chimps' ability with language still further by putting the food in containers that needed tools to be opened. In the experiments she devised, all based on the lexigram keyboard, the chimps requested a particular type of food, correctly determined the right container and the tool for opening it, opened the container and shared the food. Not only, then, can Austin and Sherman use language in order to choose and obtain a reward. They are also able to think about the best strategy for obtaining their desired ends, matching tool to task in a way that had never before been so convincingly demonstrated in the laboratory. 'The chimpanzee,' reflects Duane Rumbaugh, 'is a far more competent and capable creature than anyone thought ten years ago.'

A more recent addition to the Yerkes family of chimp speakers takes the story on yet another chapter. Kanzi is a pygmy chimp, one of the rare species *Pan paniscus*, which Sue Savage-Rumbaugh has been observing with growing astonishment. He had been in her lab for a couple of years in the company of his mother who was learning to use the computerized lexigram board. She was then taken away to breed, leaving Kanzi, now 2½ years old, on his own but with access still to the keyboard. Before long he began spontaneously to use lexigrams, choosing a symbol and then picking up the correct matching object. Unlike Austin and Sherman, who needed to be rewarded for correct behaviour, Kanzi seemed to grasp the rudiments of language exactly like a child, by being in contact with other, competent speakers. He is also relatively creative. In the course of 17 months he came out with 2805 symbolic utterances that combined two or more words. Only a tenth of these were lexigrams imitated from his trainers. The rest were his own.

Unlike Herb Terrace's Nim Chimpsky and other chimps, Kanzi also likes to point out objects just for the sake of doing so. Even if he neither wants to play with nor eat a particular thing, he will still comment on its existence. A sceptic might claim that, for all his achievements, Kanzi still possesses only an elementary level of linguistic skill compared to a human infant. But that is to miss the point. Sure enough, Kanzi lacks human facility. But he has offered enough evidence to suggest that he possesses some of the important underlying cognitive skills on which language acquisition is built.

'Fine animal gorilla'

Most studies of the intellectual capacities of chimps focus on language acquisition. And their success is usually a tribute as much to the patience and sensitivity of the researchers who do all the training as to the animals themselves. Dr Penny Patterson, for example, who runs The Gorilla Foundation in Woodside, California, has been teaching Koko since 1971 when she met the infant chimpanzee in San Francisco Zoo. During that time, and again using ASL as the vehicle of communication, Dr Patterson has imparted a claimed vocabulary of 500 words to Koko, which makes the animal perhaps the best endowed verbalizer to date.

Like other researchers, too, Dr Patterson finds that her trainee is constantly adding colour and emotion to her utterances by combining them in graphic ways. Koko seems particularly talkative when it comes to insults, with telling concoctions such as 'dirty toilet devil' or 'bad gorilla nut'. She will lie ferociously to get herself out of trouble and demonstrate a number of other streaks of character that ally her to a boisterous or naughty child. Among her qualities, too, is a graphic line in self-appreciation. 'Fine animal gorilla' is her own description of herself. Koko is therefore highly expressive. Even her use of ASL has what Dr Patterson refers to as 'a heavy gorilla accent', relying more on chimp-style body touching than would the human signer.

Coupling this fact, seen over and over again in human-chimp interactions, with the kinds of verbal skills displayed by Austin or Kanzi, it is hard not to be tempted into conceding to chimps at least a quasi-human linguistic

skill, albeit at a lower level of performance. What is less easy to admit is the possibility that apes may also possess innate mathematical ability that can be teased out by the clever experimenter.

This, however, is precisely what Dr Tetsuro Matsuzawa claims in a paper published in the scientific journal *Nature*. In it Dr Matsuzawa describes his work with a 5-year-old chimp called Ai who was trained to use Arabic numerals to specify the number of items shown to it in a special display window. The ape did this by means of a computer-linked keyboard on which were marked symbols standing for objects and colours as well as Arabic numerals from 1 to 6. It all took a lot of intensive training.

Ai had to learn to name a few objects and colours, using the symbols. Then the repertoire was increased until the chimp had mastered a vocabulary of 14 objects and 11 colours. Next the numerical component of the training was added. Ai learned just two numbers to start with, then the rest were added until the whole keyboard had been mastered.

A typical test might be to display, say, 3 red pens. Ai responds by pressing the appropriate keys for 'pen', 'red' and 'three'. She can count up to 4 objects or 4 colours with a 90% accuracy, but as the counting becomes more demanding, with 5 or 6 objects, she makes more mistakes, scoring on average 63%. It is not exactly awe-inspiring computation by human standards. Yet in these playschool-style attempts by Ai to do her sums, we can glimpse yet another important attribute: the ability to count.

This finding is, if you think about it, also slightly bizarre. Whatever its nature, there is no doubt that chimp-to-chimp communication in the wild does take place. As we have seen, chimps need to communicate, as do other species, for very important social, reproductive and cooperative purposes. So when a researcher suggests that chimps may communicate in symbolic, human-like language, we might readily understand the reasons. But why should a chimp be able to count? Does it ever need to in the wild? If so, what does it count? If not, why has evolution provided this animal with mathematical skill? Surely not to keep scientific researchers happy in their laboratories!

(*Above left*) Fast learners. The killer whale learns tricks quickly in captivity.

(*Above right*) Mind in the waters. A sea lion being taught to take and retrieve tools from divers working on the seabed.

scientists would dearly like to be able to do in order to claim that they have succeeded in programming 'intelligence' into a machine. Indeed, one definition of artificial intelligence turns on this very idea of adaptability to circumstances and surroundings.

Even deeper waters

In the light of the growing volume of observations such as those of dolphins and chimps, enthusiasts for the notion of animal thinking are less concerned than they were only a few years ago about whether other species do have thoughts in the human sense of the term. They regard this as already demonstrated. Their preoccupation now is in finding a proof that will convince the rest of us. What, they ask, do animals have to do to show us that they can think?

Perhaps the last barrier of scepticism to be broken down is that of consciousness. If animals can think, are they, like us, conscious of doing so? Are they aware of their own minds and identities? When a performing dolphin shows a sense of humour by squirting water spontaneously at its trainer, or when a chimp behaves like an affectionate (albeit spoilt) child, the people close to such animals feel intuitively that these expressive creatures 'know what they are doing'. Dog and cat lovers might say the same, as they gaze into the eyes of their pets and see there what they deem to be 'knowingness'. Is there any less anecdotal, objective evidence, though, that other animal species are self-conscious?

According to the psychologist Dr George Gallup, there are such signs in the case of chimpanzees. And he comes to this conclusion after a series of experiments designed to elicit from his animals whether they recognize themselves in a mirror. Gallup allowed some experimental chimps to familiarize themselves with mirrors, whereupon he anaesthetized them and marked their forehead and ears with bright dye. Now if this procedure is carried out with chimps that are unfamiliar with mirrors, they will pay no attention to these new facial markings. However, the animals that were used to seeing themselves in a mirror behaved quite differently. As we would do, they focused on these odd, newly arrived markings and reached out for them. Unlike chimps with no mirror experience, these animals showed by their interest in the marks that they recognized the image before them as a representation of their own bodies. Interestingly enough, this finding only seems to apply to chimps. Monkeys, gorillas and gibbons show themselves to be less 'self-conscious' in identical experiments.

Animals as psychologists

Again we are faced with an intriguing question of evolution: namely, why should some species, including our own, have evolved that quality we term 'consciousness' while others have not. According to the psychologist Dr Nicholas Humphrey, the reason why human beings are conscious is that they need to be in order to survive. Earlier in our evolutionary history, he argues, we were probably not conscious. But the nature of our social groupings soon made it imperative that each individual take account of what was going on in the minds of his or her companions. If our early ancestors were to thrive as cooperative, interdependent beings, constantly interacting with each other, they had effectively to become 'natural psychologists', tuned in to the thoughts, feelings, ambitions and preferences of others.

To do this, each individual has to form a kind of internal representation or model of other people's behaviour, and that, argues Nick Humphrey, would be impossible without having consciousness. The well-known ethologist Alison Jolly also puts forward a similar idea from her extensive work with primates, again arguing that the more complex the social interactions of a species, the more it may be driven towards evolving consciousness. Primates clearly have complicated social relationships. So too do dolphins, which are estimated to spend as much as one-third of their waking life testing and retesting their relationships. With species such as these, it is not too difficult to concede, therefore, that they may share with ourselves the faculty of self-consciousness.

Many minds

Whatever the extent of consciousness among other species, the notion proposed by Humphrey and Jolly has one very important message. It implies that animals, including humans, evolve the intellectual capacities that are consistent with their environment and lifestyle. We are conscious because consciousness fits our social needs. It is adaptive. A bee or a squid or a mynah bird likewise has just the mental apparatus it needs for its purposes. Any less would be fatal; any more superfluous. If, then, we are to learn whether other species do behave like us, thinking abstract thoughts or manipulating symbolic languages, it is essential that we observe closely what animals actually do within their own worlds and for their own purposes. The long, haunting, continuously changing songs of whales, for example, have been compared in terms of units of information to the great Homeric epic poem, the *Odyssey*. Could we take the comparison still further and speculate that these songs are indeed epics in which the whale records orally the events and even perhaps folklore of its own kind? If so, we may have to grant to other species not merely the power to communicate but to fictionalize and fantasize: not simply the need to transmit ideas in the here and now, but to pass them on for later generations in a species-specific culture. To get to that point, however, we need to know a great deal more about the communication that takes place between whales.

We can speculate better with chimpanzees. Washoe, the ASL-speaking chimp, was observed by Roger and Deborah Fouts of Central Washington University to pass on signs to an infant called Loulis, tutoring her protegée in conversations when no humans were present. Having acquired a new communication skill, Washoe then intensively transmits this to another of the coming generation. The teacher's enriched culture lives on in her pupil.

Furthermore, when Loulis and Washoe go to sleep they, like every other mammal (except, curiously, the spiny anteater) and many non-mammalian species, will enter into phases of rapid eye movement – REM – the times when dreaming takes place. What dreams do chimps have? Are their nocturnal dramas like ours, a fantastic hotch-potch of imagery and events strung together into overwhelmingly graphic adventures?

Here too we may have an insight gleaned by a clever experimenter, this time not with large-brained chimps or dolphins but with the domestic cat. In his laboratory at the University of Lyon, in France, Professor Michel Jouvet has been able surgically to modify the nervous system of cats in such a way that, during REM phases, they appear to 'act out' what they are dreaming. As the machine tells the experimenter that the sleeping cat is in REM, it starts up, still asleep, then crouches and attempts to spring at imaginary mice, as if rehearsing a basic feline predation strategy. As 'natural psychologists', perhaps that is what we are doing in our dreams, in our case rehearsing social strategies for the days ahead. Many of our dreams involve other people. Are we then programmed to represent ourselves constantly in private social dramas during sleep so that we may be better equipped publicly to face the day?

Nature likes to work in universals sticking to a restricted number of tried and tested designs and principles. And this is not surprising. We share with other animals the same planet. Why should we not share, too, at least some of the same basic internal patterns and procedures? In this book we have repeatedly found parallels between animals and humans. This is not to declare that they must be clever or intelligent because they are like us. It is to underscore the ineradicable fact that we are all part of a massive family tree. But there are no topmost branches.

One final word, though, on the question of animal intelligence. Perhaps the ultimate proof, which would silence the doubters for all time, would be unequivocal evidence that a member of some species other than our own was an ethologist, as well as a psychologist, and was using its mental apparatus to decide whether *we* are really intelligent animals. Were the tables to be turned, what results, one wonders, would such observations yield?

Glossary

ADAPTATION The adjustment of a species to changing environmental conditions. If a feature of an animal fits the circumstances prevailing, it tends to be retained; if not, it is 'maladaptive', and tends to perish with the animals that possess it. Darwin's 'survival of the fittest' means the 'survival of the best-adapted'.

AGGRESSION Ethologists have long debated the meaning of 'aggression'. At its most general, aggression may be thought of as any behaviour that intimidates or harms another organism. Often, however, predation is excluded, while defensive or property-protective behaviour is not.

ALTRUISM Behaviour that benefits another individual to the detriment (or apparent detriment) of the animal that performs it. Sometimes the altruistic animal does benefit too: if the receiver is related to the altruist then the latter's genes are, partly, promoted by its behaviour. 'Reciprocal altruism' occurs when the altruist stands to gain, say, from a social partner that will later reciprocate.

ARTHROPOD There are twelve classes of arthropod, including insects, centipedes, crustaceans, spiders. Eighty-five per cent of all animal species belong to this phylum (see Phylogeny).

CELL The smallest unit of living matter and from which all animals are formed. The amoeba consists of just one cell; a multicellular organism such as a human is an organized population of billions of cells. Like the organisms themselves, cells take in food, excrete waste, and reproduce. Within the nucleus of the cell lies the genetic material in the form of DNA.

CETACEAN A mammalian order that embraces whales, porpoises and dolphins.

COMMUNICATION In its broadest sense, communication can be thought of as behaviour of one animal that influences that of another. Usually this involves the sending of signals or messages. It also implies some kind of 'intent' on the part of the sender, because an inadvertent signal (such as a mouse betraying its presence by rustling the grass) is usually not thought of as communication. On the other hand we cannot say that the sender of the message 'means' to communicate with others.

CRUSTACEAN A large class of arthropods including crabs, crayfish, prawns, lobster, shrimps, sandhopper, woodlice, water fleas, krill.

DISPLAY Movement patterns of a stereotyped nature used in communication. Usually these are confined to a species and are involved in courtship, mating, threat and aggression. Displays are important communications strategies, synchronizing the behaviour of mating pairs, for example, or ensuring that members of different species do not cross-breed. As well as having a social function, a display may also represent a predator – prey signal. A predator may lure a prey with bodily features that look attractive; or a potential prey may deter predators by displaying markings or other features that misleadingly make it look threatening.

DOMINANCE Some animals, often older and stronger individuals, acquire higher status than others in their societies. This gives them access to resources such as food, space and mates. Subordinates may be kept in place in the social hierarchy by the aggressive behaviour of dominants, but sometimes they defer unilaterally.

DOPPLER (effect) Changes in pitch in sound according to whether an object is approaching or receding. If the latter, pitch is reduced; if the former, raised.

ETHOLOGY The study of animal behaviour, combining observations of various forms of behaviour with ideas about how these are caused and what may be their function. Although there is a long naturalist tradition, modern ethology began comparatively recently. The three great pioneers of the subject – Karl von Frisch, Konrad Lorenz and Niko Tinbergen – were awarded the Nobel Prize (for Medicine) in 1973.

EVOLUTION The process by which new species of organism arise. The fossil record shows a progression of animal forms over millions of years, from simpler to more complex creatures. In the rocks we can 'see' evolution taking place. The actual mechanism of evolution, though, is not universally agreed upon. Charles Darwin's theory of natural selection described evolution as the gradual emergence of those natural mutations best adapted to environmental conditions. But some people argue against gradualism as the only process, putting the case for jumps in evolution – 'punctuated equilibrium' – echoed by undeniable gaps in the fossil record.

FREQUENCY The number of vibrations (cycles) per second of a sound wave. The tone of a sound is determined by its frequency. The lower the frequency, the lower the tone, and vice versa.

GENE Biochemical units of inheritance that transmit, from one generation to the next, information in coded form which controls the development, appearance and to some extent behaviour of an organism. The genetic code is based on the sequence of chemicals in the molecule deoxyribonucleic acid – DNA – packed within the nucleus of cells.

HIERARCHY A pyramid-style social structure with dominant animals enjoying greater benefits than subordinates. Maintaining or establishing a position in a hierarchy is an important feature of animal behaviour.

INSTINCT (instinctive behaviour) Behaviour which is inborn and fixed. Ethologists tend to use the term quite rarely nowadays because it often gives a misleading impression of behaviour that exists without any need for an animal to copy and learn from others.

INVESTMENT The amount of energy expended by a parent on the young. This may take place even before fertilization, though usually the term is applied to feeding and caring for offspring once born. Although males may be involved in the process, the burden of investment usually falls on female animals.

LANGUAGE Sometimes 'language' is used to describe only the communication system of humans, but in this book it is applied to various types of animal-to-animal message-sending. Thus, language here can mean anything from the song of a bird to the dance of a bee. Not all animal languages have every feature of human language. We use symbols, can combine words creatively and express ideas and information about events remote in space and time. Not every animal can do that. On the other hand, there is evidence that we may share those features with a few other species.

LEARNING A change in behaviour in response to a change in an animal's environment. Ethologists can usually only infer that an animal has learned something from the way it behaves. So if a rat correctly runs a maze to get a food reward when initially it did not, we might say it has learned to find food. Several different kinds of learning have been identified; imitation is one, so too is conditioning whereby an animal (such as the rat in the maze) is directed by the process of stimulus-response-reinforcement.

PHEROMONE A communicating chemical passing from one animal to another and eliciting a behavioural reaction or change in the receiver's physiological state.

PHYLOGENY (phylogenetic) The formal classification of animals into generic groupings or phyla. There are 38 phyla of animals, subdivided into classes, then into orders, families, genera and species.

PRIMATE The mammalian order which includes lemurs, monkeys, apes and humans.

SELECTION The natural pressure on some animals to survive – being the best-adapted to their environment – and on others to perish. The basis of modern evolutionary theory, natural selection was discussed by Charles Darwin in his book, published in 1859, *On the Origin of Species by Means of Natural Selection, or the Preservation of Favoured Races in the Struggle for Survival.*

SOCIETY Social organization of animals, ranging from cooperation between a pair or a few individuals to complex relationships such as one finds among large numbers of ants. There are many kinds of social relationships and interactions; communication usually plays a major role in establishing and maintaining them.

SOCIOBIOLOGY The study of the biological origins and evolution of social behaviour.

SONAR (echo-location) An abbreviation for Sound Navigation And Ranging. A technique for obtaining information about phenomena or objects underwater. It depends on emitting sound waves in pulses and, from the timing and direction of the echoes, being able to determine range and bearing of a target object.

SPECIES Genetically similar animals which can usually only breed with each other, but not with other species, to produce viable offspring.

TERRITORY An area occupied and defended by an animal or animals.

VERTEBRATE An animal with a backbone. In the phylogenetic scale, *Vertebrata* are a sub-phylum of the phylum *Chordata*.

Bibliography

Anderson, E. W. *Animals as Navigators* (Bodley Head, 1983)

Barloy, J. J. *Man and Animals* (Gordon and Cremonesi, 1978)

Bateson, P. (ed). *Mate Choice* (Cambridge University Press, 1983)

Beck, A. and Katcher, A. *Between Pets and People* (G. P. Putnam's Sons, 1983)

Birch, M. C. and Haynes, K. F. *Insect Pheromones* (Edward Arnold, 1982)

Blakemore, C. *Mechanics of the Mind* (Cambridge University Press, 1977)

Bright, M. *Animal Language* (BBC, 1984)

Catchpole, C. K. *Vocal Communication in Birds* (Edward Arnold, 1979)

Cloudsley-Thompson, J. L. *Tooth and Claw* (J. M. Dent, 1980)

Colman, A. *Cooperation and Competition in Humans and Animals* (Von Nostrand Reinhold [UK], 1982)

Crail, T. *Apetalk and Whalespeak* (Contemporary Books, 1983)

Dawkins, R. *The Selfish Gene* (Oxford University Press, 1976)

De Waal, F. *Chimpanzee Politics* (Unwin Paperbacks, 1982)

Evans, C. and Evans, P. *Landscapes of the Night* (Victor Gollancz, 1983)

Ferry, G. (ed). *The Understanding of Animals* (Basil Blackwell and New Scientist, 1984)

Griffin, D. R. *Animal Thinking* (Harvard University Press, 1984)

Griffin, D. R. *Echoes of Bats and Men* (Doubleday [Anchor], 1959)

Griffin, D. R. *The Question of Animal Awareness* (Rockefeller University Press, 1981)

Halliday, T. R. *Sexual Strategy* (Oxford University Press, 1980)

Halliday, T. R. and Slater, R. J. B. (eds). *Animal Behaviour: Volume 2; Communications* (Blackwell Scientific, 1983)

Halliday, T. R. and Slater, R. J. B. (eds). *Animal Behaviour: Volume 3; Genes, Development and Learning* (Blackwell Scientific, 1983)

Hansell, M. H. *Animal Architecture and Building Behaviour* (Longman, 1984)

Hinde, R. A. *Biological Bases of Human Social Behaviour* (McGraw-Hill, 1974)

Hinde, R. A. *Ethology* (Fontana Paperback, 1982)

Jolly, A. *The Evolution of Primate Behaviour* (Macmillan [Collier Macmillan Publishers], 1985)

Kavanagh, M. *A Complete Guide to Monkeys, Apes and Other Primates* (Jonathan Cape, 1983)

Kilpatrick, C. *Animals of the World* (Hamlyn, 1977)

McFarland, D. (ed). *The Oxford Companion to Animal Behaviour* (Oxford University Press, 1981)

Manning, A. *An Introduction to Animal Behaviour* (Edward Arnold, 1972)

Matthews, L. H. (ed). *The Whale* (George Allen and Unwin, 1968)

Nollman, J. *Dolphin Dreamtime* (Anthony Blond, 1985)

O'Neill, G. K. *The High Frontier* (Jonathan Cape, 1976)

Owen, D. *Camouflage and Mimicry* (Oxford University Press, 1980)

Passingham, R. E. *The Human Primate* (W. H. Freeman, 1982)

Poole, T. *Social Behaviour in Mammals* (Blackie, 1985)

Richelle, M. and Lejeune, H. *Time in Animal Behaviour* (Pergamon Press, 1980)

Rose, S. and Appignanesi, L. (eds). *Science and Beyond* (Blackwell, 1986)

Russell, F. *The Hunting Animal* (Hutchinson, 1984)

Sagan, C. *Cosmos* (Macdonald, 1980)

Schaller, G. B. *The Serengeti Lion* (University of Chicago Press, 1972)

Serpell, J. *In the Company of Animals* (Blackwell, 1986)

Slater, P. J. B. (ed). *The Collins Encyclopedia of Animal Behaviour* (Collins, 1986)

Thomas, K. *Man and the Natural World* (Penguin, 1984)

Thorpe, W. H. *Animal Nature and Human Nature* (Methuen, 1974)

Walker, S. *Animal Thought* (Routledge and Kegan Paul, 1983)

Wilson, E. O. *Biophilia* (Harvard University Press, 1984)

Wilson, E. O. *Sociobiology: the new synthesis* (Harvard University Press, 1975)

Wilson, E. O. *The Insect Societies* (The Belknap Press of Harvard University Press, 1971)

Acknowledgements

In the space of around fifty years ethology – the study of animal behaviour – has gone from being an amateur hobbyist's pastime to an established scientific discipline. The old-style naturalist, with his binoculars and country tweed jacket, has given way to, or rather been joined by, the professional student of animal behaviour who often adds to keen observation high-technology methods of experimentation and analysis. Both old style and new though remain fundamentally one and the same animal. Both share an unwavering sense of pleasure, indeed wonderment, at the ever-surprising behaviour of their chosen species. In the first instance it is with enormous gratitude that I acknowledge the patience and insight that ethologists of all colours have brought to their subject. I hope this book reflects fairly some of their efforts.

Thanks are due also to: the production team at Harcourt Films – Jeremy Marre, Alice Harper and Maurice Melzack – for their advice and encouragement; to Gerald and Lee Durrell for detailed suggestions on my first draft; Liz Harcourt for her able picture research and help with captions; my publishers, especially Anthony Lambert, for extreme calm in the face of a tight production schedule; and finally my wife Ann and children Kate and Ben for bearing with a frequently preoccupied husband and father.

P.E., London,
1987

Index

Photograph Acknowledgements

The publishers would like to thank the following individuals and organizations for permission to reproduce photographs:

page 1 Bill Wood/Bruce Coleman Ltd; 2/3 Alistair Shay/Oxford Scientific Films; 11 Colorsport; 12 (*above left*) Gordon Langsbury/Bruce Coleman Ltd; (*above right*) Hans Reinhard/Bruce Coleman Ltd; (*below*) Gordon Langsbury/Bruce Coleman Ltd; 14 Ronald Thompson/Frank W Lane/Bruce Coleman Ltd; 16 J. Mackinnin/Bruce Coleman Ltd; 17 Mark N Boulton/Bruce Coleman Ltd; 18 Ardea London Ltd; 19 Illustrated London News Picture Library; 21 P. Morris/Ardea London Ltd; 23 Jean-Paul Ferrero/Ardea London Ltd; 24 F. Jack Jackson/Planet Earth Pictures; 25 Mike Coltman/Planet Earth Pictures; 27 (*above*) Philip Sharpe/Oxford Scientific Films; (*below*) David Thompson/Oxford Scientific Films; 29 Stephen Dalton/NHPA; 32 (*left*) Dr Frieder Sauer/Bruce Coleman Ltd; (*right*) John Hawkins/Eric & David Hosking; 33 David Thompson/Oxford Scientific Films; 35 G. Ziesler/Bruce Coleman Ltd; 38 Patrick Baker/Bruce Coleman Ltd; 40/41 Michael Fogden/Oxford Scientific Films; 45 Horace Kinloch/Aquila Photographics; 47 S. Meyers/Ardea London Ltd; 50 Jane Burton/Bruce Coleman Ltd; 51 G. Zeisler/Bruce Coleman Ltd; 54/55 G. Zeisler/Bruce Coleman Ltd; 57 Anthony Bannister/NHPA; 58 Wayne Lankinen/Bruce Coleman Ltd; 61 Hans and Judy Beste/Area London Ltd; 62 Lacz Lemoine/NHPA; 63 Peter Davey/Bruce Coleman Ltd; 65 (*left*) Dieter and Mary Plage/Bruce Coleman Ltd; (*right*) Helmut Albrecht/Bruce Coleman Ltd; 66 P. J. Devries; 68 Warren Williams/Planet Earth Pictures; 69 M. Malzak/Harcourt Films Ltd; 70 S. Bolwell/Agilis Pictures; 71 K. W. Fink/Ardea London Ltd; 73 P. A. Hinchliffe/Bruce Coleman Ltd; 74 Anthony Bannister/NHPA; 75 Harcourt Films; 78 Richard Matthews/Seaphot Ltd/Planet Earth Pictures; 79 Rod Williams/Bruce Coleman Ltd; 81 Brian Coates/Bruce Coleman Ltd; 83 J. A. L. Cooke/Oxford Scientific Films; 86/87 Jonathan Scott/Seaphot Ltd/Planet Earth Pictures; 88 Joseph Van Wormer/Bruce Coleman Ltd; 90 Bruce Coleman/Bruce Coleman Ltd; 93 François Gohier/Ardea London Ltd; 94 Hans Reinhard/Bruce Coleman Ltd; 97 K. Lindsay/Cambridge University; 98 Jon Kenfield/Bruce Coleman Ltd; 99 A. H. Harcourt/Cambridge University; 101 John Visser/Bruce Coleman Ltd; 103 Doug Allan/Oxford Scientific Films; 106 Michael Fogden/Oxford Scientific Films; 107 Jen and Des Bartlett/Survival Anglia; 108/109 P. & W. Ward/Oxford Scientific Films; 111 J. A. L. Cooke/Oxford Scientific Films; 112 Jane Burton/Bruce Coleman Ltd; 113 Jane Burton/Bruce Coleman Ltd; 114 Jane Burton/Bruce Coleman Ltd; 116 Mike Wilkes; 117 M. P. Kahl/Bruce Coleman Ltd; 118 Dennis Green/Bruce Coleman Ltd; 123 Gerald Cubitt/Bruce Coleman Ltd; 126 Mike Roberts; 127 Brian Seed/Aspect Picture Library; 128 Jane Burton/Bruce Coleman Ltd; 129 Hellio & VanIngen/NHPA; 131 François Gohier/Ardea London Ltd; 132 Francisco Erize/Bruce Coleman Ltd; 134 Kim Taylor/Bruce Coleman Ltd; 137 Jane Burton/Bruce Coleman Ltd; 138 (*above*) Arthus-Bertrand/Ardea London Ltd; Alan Root/Bruce Coleman Ltd; (*below*) Mark N. Boulton/ICCE; 140 Arthus-Bertrand/Ardea London Ltd; 142 Frans Lanting/Bruce Coleman Ltd; 146 (*left*) John Shaw/Bruce Coleman Ltd; (*right*) Norman Myers/Bruce Coleman Ltd; 148 Cindy Buxton and Annie Price/Survival Anglia Ltd; 150 Adrian Warren/Ardea London Ltd; 151 K. Ammann/Seaphot Ltd/Planet Earth Pictures; 152 Simon Trevor/Bruce Coleman Ltd; 153 Sylvia Harcourt/Survival Anglia Ltd; 154 Norman Myers/Bruce Coleman Ltd; 156 Manfred Danegger/NHPA; 158 Jen and Des Bartlett/Survival Anglia Ltd; 159 Frithfoto/Bruce Coleman Ltd; 161 S. Robinson/NHPA; 162 D. C. Houston/Bruce Coleman Ltd; 164 Michael Fogden/Oxford Scientific Films; 167 J. P. Ferrero/Ardea London Ltd; 170 Wayne Lankinen/Aquila Photographics; 172 John Daniels/Ardea London Ltd; 175 Ian Beames/Ardea London Ltd; 176 (*above*) Paul Sterry/Nature Photographers Ltd; (*below*) Peter Johnson/NHPA; 177 I. Wyllie/Harcourt Films; 178 Harcourt Films; 179 Alice Harper/Harcourt Films; 182 Marc Henrie; 183 Marc Henrie; 184 Jeremy Marre/Harcourt Films; 186 Rex Features; 187 (*above*) Hans Reinhard/Bruce Coleman Ltd; (*below*) Alice Harper/Harcourt Films; 188 Hans Christian Heap/Seaphot Ltd/Planet Earth Pictures; 191 (*above*) John Moss/Colorific; (*below*) Eddie Adams/Colorific; 193 (*above*) Kim Taylor/Bruce Coleman Ltd; (*below*) M. P. L. Fogden/Bruce Coleman Ltd; 194 David W. MacDonald/Oxford Scientific Films; 195 Jane Burton/Bruce Coleman Ltd; 201 W. Boyle, Department of Biological Sciences, Purdue University; 203 Yerkes Regional Primate Research Center of Emory University; 204 Peter Davey/Bruce Coleman Ltd; 207 (*left*) Flip Schulke/Seaphot Ltd; (*right*) François Gohier/Ardea London Ltd

Diagrams by Ian Sandom

Photograph Acknowledgements

The publishers would like to thank the following individuals and organizations for permission to reproduce photographs:

page 1 Bill Wood/Bruce Coleman Ltd; 2/3 Alistair Shay/Oxford Scientific Films; 11 Colorsport; 12 (*above left*) Gordon Langsbury/Bruce Coleman Ltd; (*above right*) Hans Reinhard/Bruce Coleman Ltd; (*below*) Gordon Langsbury/Bruce Coleman Ltd; 14 Ronald Thompson/Frank W Lane/Bruce Coleman Ltd; 16 J. Mackinnin/Bruce Coleman Ltd; 17 Mark N Boulton/Bruce Coleman Ltd; 18 Ardea London Ltd; 19 Illustrated London News Picture Library; 21 P. Morris/Ardea London Ltd; 23 Jean-Paul Ferrero/Ardea London Ltd; 24 F. Jack Jackson/Planet Earth Pictures; 25 Mike Coltman/Planet Earth Pictures; 27 (*above*) Philip Sharpe/Oxford Scientific Films; (*below*) David Thompson/Oxford Scientific Films; 29 Stephen Dalton/NHPA; 32 (*left*) Dr Frieder Sauer/Bruce Coleman Ltd; (*right*) John Hawkins/Eric & David Hosking; 33 David Thompson/Oxford Scientific Films; 35 G. Ziesler/Bruce Coleman Ltd; 38 Patrick Baker/Bruce Coleman Ltd; 40/41 Michael Fogden/Oxford Scientific Films; 45 Horace Kinloch/Aquila Photographics; 47 S. Meyers/Ardea London Ltd; 50 Jane Burton/Bruce Coleman Ltd; 51 G. Zeisler/Bruce Coleman Ltd; 54/55 G. Zeisler/Bruce Coleman Ltd; 57 Anthony Bannister/NHPA; 58 Wayne Lankinen/Bruce Coleman Ltd; 61 Hans and Judy Beste/Area London Ltd; 62 Lacz Lemoine/NHPA; 63 Peter Davey/Bruce Coleman Ltd; 65 (*left*) Dieter and Mary Plage/Bruce Coleman Ltd; (*right*) Helmut Albrecht/Bruce Coleman Ltd; 66 P. J. Devries; 68 Warren Williams/Planet Earth Pictures; 69 M. Malzak/Harcourt Films Ltd; 70 S. Bolwell/Agilis Pictures; 71 K. W. Fink/Ardea London Ltd; 73 P. A. Hinchliffe/Bruce Coleman Ltd; 74 Anthony Bannister/NHPA; 75 Harcourt Films; 78 Richard Matthews/Seaphot Ltd/Planet Earth Pictures; 79 Rod Williams/Bruce Coleman Ltd; 81 Brian Coates/Bruce Coleman Ltd; 83 J. A. L. Cooke/Oxford Scientific Films; 86/87 Jonathan Scott/Seaphot Ltd/Planet Earth Pictures; 88 Joseph Van Wormer/Bruce Coleman Ltd; 90 Bruce Coleman/Bruce Coleman Ltd; 93 François Gohier/Ardea London Ltd; 94 Hans Reinhard/Bruce Coleman Ltd; 97 K. Lindsay/Cambridge University; 98 Jon Kenfield/Bruce Coleman Ltd; 99 A. H. Harcourt/Cambridge University; 101 John Visser/Bruce Coleman Ltd; 103 Doug Allan/Oxford Scientific Films; 106 Michael Fogden/Oxford Scientific Films; 107 Jen and Des Bartlett/Survival Anglia; 108/109 P. & W. Ward/Oxford Scientific Films; 111 J. A. L. Cooke/Oxford Scientific Films; 112 Jane Burton/Bruce Coleman Ltd; 113 Jane Burton/Bruce Coleman Ltd; 114 Jane Burton/Bruce Coleman Ltd; 116 Mike Wilkes; 117 M. P. Kahl/Bruce Coleman Ltd; 118 Dennis Green/Bruce Coleman Ltd; 123 Gerald Cubitt/Bruce Coleman Ltd; 126 Mike Roberts; 127 Brian Seed/Aspect Picture Library; 128 Jane Burton/Bruce Coleman Ltd; 129 Hellio & VanIngen/NHPA; 131 François Gohier/Ardea London Ltd; 132 Francisco Erize/Bruce Coleman Ltd; 134 Kim Taylor/Bruce Coleman Ltd; 137 Jane Burton/Bruce Coleman Ltd; 138 (*above*) Arthus-Bertrand/Ardea London Ltd; Alan Root/Bruce Coleman Ltd; (*below*) Mark N. Boulton/ICCE; 140 Arthus-Bertrand/Ardea London Ltd; 142 Frans Lanting/Bruce Coleman Ltd; 146 (*left*) John Shaw/Bruce Coleman Ltd; (*right*) Norman Myers/Bruce Coleman Ltd; 148 Cindy Buxton and Annie Price/Survival Anglia Ltd; 150 Adrian Warren/Ardea London Ltd; 151 K. Ammann/Seaphot Ltd/Planet Earth Pictures; 152 Simon Trevor/Bruce Coleman Ltd; 153 Sylvia Harcourt/Survival Anglia Ltd; 154 Norman Myers/Bruce Coleman Ltd; 156 Manfred Danegger/NHPA; 158 Jen and Des Bartlett/Survival Anglia Ltd; 159 Frithfoto/Bruce Coleman Ltd; 161 S. Robinson/NHPA; 162 D. C. Houston/Bruce Coleman Ltd; 164 Michael Fogden/Oxford Scientific Films; 167 J. P. Ferrero/Ardea London Ltd; 170 Wayne Lankinen/Aquila Photographics; 172 John Daniels/Ardea London Ltd; 175 Ian Beames/Ardea London Ltd; 176 (*above*) Paul Sterry/Nature Photographers Ltd; (*below*) Peter Johnson/NHPA; 177 I. Wyllie/Harcourt Films; 178 Harcourt Films; 179 Alice Harper/Harcourt Films; 182 Marc Henrie; 183 Marc Henrie; 184 Jeremy Marre/Harcourt Films; 186 Rex Features; 187 (*above*) Hans Reinhard/Bruce Coleman Ltd; (*below*) Alice Harper/Harcourt Films; 188 Hans Christian Heap/Seaphot Ltd/Planet Earth Pictures; 191 (*above*) John Moss/Colorific; (*below*) Eddie Adams/Colorific; 193 (*above*) Kim Taylor/Bruce Coleman Ltd; (*below*) M. P. L. Fogden/Bruce Coleman Ltd; 194 David W. MacDonald/Oxford Scientific Films; 195 Jane Burton/Bruce Coleman Ltd; 201 W. Boyle, Department of Biological Sciences, Purdue University; 203 Yerkes Regional Primate Research Center of Emory University; 204 Peter Davey/Bruce Coleman Ltd; 207 (*left*) Flip Schulke/Seaphot Ltd; (*right*) François Gohier/Ardea London Ltd

Diagrams by Ian Sandom